The Prince of Thieves

George Manolesco as smart Prince Lahovary on holiday in Lucerne, 1898

The Prince of Thieves

A BIOGRAPHY OF

George Manolesco

ALIAS

H. H. Prince Lahovary

ALIAS

The Duke of Otranto

J. J. LYNX

ATHENEUM   NEW YORK   1964

Author's Preface

For the advice and assistance given to me when collecting the material for this biography of George Manolesco I am greatly obliged to lawyers, judges and police officials in many countries, and to journalists and writers, especially the late Mr. C. M. Schmidt, chief crime reporter of the Ullstein Publishing House in Berlin, and to the late Fritz Wolff, the cartoonist who illustrated the trial in Berlin and later had many talks with Manolesco in Paris. Valuable sources of information were also French, German, Romanian and Italian newspapers of the time and the *Memoirs of Prince Lahovary*; a pungent book by the State Prosecutor of Saxonia, Dr. Erich Wulffen, on the 'arch-liar' George Manolesco; and the report in Friedlander's *Famous Criminal Trials*.

My greatest helper, however, was the late Dr. Heinz Braun, an officer of the *Kriminalpolizei* in the VIIIth Precinct of Vienna. He collected 'freaks of humanity' as other people collect matchboxes or butterflies. He made the Manolesco case his great hobby and supplied the material for many stories such as the episodes in Constantinople, Nice, Vienna, Budapest and the United States. Some of the pictures published here are from his collection, much of which was destroyed by the Nazis when they invaded Austria and killed Dr. Braun.

For obvious reasons the names of some of the people involved and the names of some localities have been changed —even George's name is changed, for originally it was Georgiu Mercadente Manulescu. In Paris he simplified his name, insisting that nobody in France could pronounce the original properly! Other than certain dialogue passages which necessarily had to be reconstructed, the story of George Manolesco is told here for the first time with adherence to the facts.

Lastly I would like to express my sincere appreciation to Mr. J. P. Gallagher for his unfailing help and advice, without which this book could not have been written.

J. J. L.

The Prince of Thieves

Chapter 1

'Gogu!' Grandmother called upstairs in her thin voice that always sounded frustrated and sad. 'Get up and dress. You have to fetch your father. Breakfast is on the table.'

Grandmother always called him 'Gogu', which he hated. She never called him George or Georgiu, as one addressed a man. But then she hated the Romanian language which, she said, was a bad imitation of French, and she spoke only in the language of Voltaire and Molière, whom she adored.

George got up slowly, walked over to the small tin basin on the window-sill and wetted his face and hands perfunctorily, drying himself with a frayed towel. He put on his clothes, raced out of the narrow attic room and jumped down the steep stairs to the kitchen.

Grandmother was standing at the little oil stove, stirring the maize *polenta*. The floor of the kitchen was covered with oil-cloth worn thin and in parts the floorboards were visible. On the white, scrubbed wooden table in the middle stood a chipped cup and plate, a steaming pot of tea and a basket with dark, brown bread. Four chairs held together by string and wire and the rusty oil stove were the entire furniture.

The old woman did not even turn her head when George bounced into the kitchen, but went on stirring. Her silver hair was neatly tucked under a head scarf; she had on a faded blue dress that was spotlessly clean. She was small and fragile but held herself very erect.

George mumbled, 'Bon jour, gran'mère,' pulled out a chair and sat down. The table wobbled. It had wobbled as long as George could remember. One of its legs was shorter than the other three and as usual the folded piece of paper, which was pushed underneath to keep the balance, had slipped out. George bent down and pushed it back under the leg. Father had promised a hundred times to repair the table, and always forgotten to do it, just as he had promised to have the broken window repaired and the paint on the walls renewed. But the window was still boarded up with a piece of wood and the paint flaked off the walls.

Grandmother put down a cracked earthen bowl filled with steaming maize and added some cold milk from a tin pitcher. There was no sugar. Sugar was expensive and therefore not much used in the Manolesco *ménage*. George started eating rapidly and greedily, poured himself a beaker full of hot tea and dipped a slice of the dark bread into the steaming cup.

'Don't eat like a pig,' said Grandmother tartly. 'Eat with manners, like a gentleman.'

George looked around the small, shabby kitchen and its marks of poverty, then at Grandmother who looked back at him severely, and spooned his food more slowly. When he had finished he put his chair back under the table, took his used cup, spoon and bowl to the basin under the window-sill, and washed them.

As soon as his grandmother went upstairs, he sneaked out of the kitchen into the garden. At the end of a narrow strip of neglected grass, screened from the house by some overgrown bushes, stood a small shed. Here George kept his treasures: bits of string, coins, pebbles, marbles, a broken knife he had found on the way to school, and most precious of all, about a pound of candy sugar which he had acquired through a long process of trading.

From the priest of the parish church he had received a coloured picture with glass dust sprayed over the saint's robe, which made it the envy of all his classmates. Aspasiu, next door, was especially keen to have the wonderful picture and managed to get it in exchange for two wheels from an old alarm clock and fourteen vari-coloured pebbles. George kept the broken wheels and exchanged twelve of the pebbles with Alexandre for candy sugar, which Alexandre stole from his father's grocery store. Carefully now he took the sugar out of the tiny gap under the roof, which was his secret safe, broke off a small piece and returned the rest to the hiding-place. From the kitchen Grandmother called. He put the piece of sugar into his pocket and ran back to the house.

A few minutes later he was on his way along the dusty road to collect his father from the barracks.

Fetching his father home in the morning was not a new experience for George. Lately it had been as often as four times a week. Father, who had fought in the Romanian–Russian–Turkish war of 1879 was a captain in a cavalry regiment, but had been sent from Bucharest to Ploesti, to the 32nd Infantry Regiment of the 9th Brigade of the Royal Romanian Army. His annual salary was worth perhaps £400 in today's money and was all too small to maintain a home and family, his horses and the elaborate uniforms of the day. He became a gambler, but an unsuccessful one—his transfer was more or less a standard punishment for officers who ran up large debts and lived too gay a life in the Romanian capital.

When George was born on May 20, 1871, his father was thirty-five years old and his mother eighteen. She died two years later. Now Captain Manolesco was a lonely and bitter man, dreading going home in the evenings to the austerity of the little cottage behind the barrack walls, and the constant nagging of his eighty-year-old mother. He stayed on in the officers' mess where there was always good company and a game of cards. Luck seldom favoured Captain Manolesco, and when George arrived in the mornings, he generally found a dispirited man, full of *Slivovitz* but with empty pockets, whom he had to support on his way home, to be sobered up and tidied by Grandmother so that he could appear properly at the morning roll-call of the regiment.

George liked the officers' mess, and went there often after school. He would sit silently for hours watching the card players, fascinated by the colourful little pictures on the cards. Sometimes he begged one of the orderlies to give him an old pack to take home to his attic, where he played imaginary games with imaginary partners. The officers were very amused by the interest the boy showed in their games and occasionally performed for him simple card-tricks. George picked these up very quickly and after a time could do them much better than the men.

His greatest friend was the orderly-sergeant Carol Tiriu. As a young man, and before he had joined the army, Tiriu had been a stage magician, but had to give up his career when he lost a little finger in a brawl. Despite his mutilated hand he could still perform enough tricks to astonish George. He taught the eager boy all the tricks he could and described others he himself could no longer perform. At the age of eight George knew all the games played in the mess and could certainly play them better than his father. Cards mysteriously and magically obeyed his long, sensitive fingers. At the annual officers' dance in the Town Hall of Ploesti, George performed card-tricks in the cabaret to the amazement of the guests. His gambling teacher had to confess that his pupil could now perform many more tricks than he had ever known and he predicted a great future for George.

George, however, was not interested in the future. He lived in the present and had a very practical use for his acquired knowledge and natural skill. Soon enough he discovered the power of money, of which some had plenty and others had none. When he arrived at the mess he would see young tightly-corseted officers from rich families being collected by smartly dressed grooms and valets to be taken home in private carriages, while his father had to stumble through the dust or mud of the barrack square. He would stare at the glittering carriages drawn by beautifully-groomed horses. One day *he* would own a carriage like that, with a groom *and* a valet to take care of his needs.

One afternoon he arrived at the playground in the park with a pack of cards and soon a small circle of boys squatted under the oak trees and listened to George as he explained vingt-et-un to them. It is a simple game and the boys understood quickly. At first they played for fun, then for pebbles, in the end for money. Many of his schoolmates came from wealthy families and received ample pocket money. George soon won all their money.

'Lend us some money back,' said the boys. 'We want to go on playing so that we can get back what we have lost.'

George was always obliging. He graciously lent his friends some of their lost money, so that they could lose it again. When they had to confess that they had forfeited their pocket money for weeks to come, he suggested that they should stake any valuables they possessed, a golden cross on a chain around the neck, or a pen-knife, or a watch.

Most of the money he won was spent satisfying his craving for sweets, or going to the circus. He kept his mentor Tiriu supplied with cigars and tobacco, not because he felt any gratitude for the man who had showed him one way to riches, but because of the desire to show off, a desire which developed with the years into a mania for grandeur.

Then the storm broke. Parents of some boys had complained for some time that costly trinkets were disappearing from their houses. They never even dreamed that their own boys could have anything to do with the matter and that everything had found its way to George in endless and fruitless attempts to win back lost money. But one day the father of a classmate, and a very influential man, discovered in a junk-shop window in the slums of the town a gold chain with a ruby cross which he recognized at once as belonging to his daughter. The man who owned the shop, frightened by the threat to call the police, confessed that he had bought it from a boy, and returned it to its rightful owner. The boy, who had taken the cross from his sister's room, denied everything, but then other valuable objects were discovered by parents in similar shops. Some of the traders were able to describe the seller, and their accounts all pointed straight to George Manolesco. A number of the parents went together to Captain Manolesco's commanding officer. Under pressure from the most influential men in the town, he summoned the Captain and ordered him to remove George from the town before every boy in the place was corrupted.

'The boy should be handed over to the police,' he said, 'but I have persuaded the parents that such a step would be more damaging to you, Captain, than to the boy. George must be kept under strict control from now on. No more visits to the officers' mess, no more fiddling with playing cards. His headmaster has agreed to keep the boy at school, until you find somewhere else for him to go.'

This was a terrible blow to Captain Manolesco's honour. He locked George up in his attic with bread and water only. A firmer hand than Grandmother's was needed to keep the boy out of mischief. As a soldier he could think of nothing more effective than severe military discipline and hard training. The army should have been the obvious choice for a professional soldier's son but the army did not stand in too high esteem with Captain Manolesco. One had to be very rich to make a career in the army where the pay was bad, and bribery and buying of favours a common occurrence. The Captain did not want for his only son a future as drab and poverty-stricken as his own. With her newly-received independence, Romania, under a German-born King, Carol I, was starting to build up a new navy. Captain Manolesco decided on a naval career for George and enlisted him at the Establishment for Training of Officer Cadets in Galatz on the Danube estuary, near the Black Sea.

George shed no tears on leaving Ploesti. He had always hated the town, smelling as it did of petroleum from the nearby deposits. He hated his own poverty and the narrow-minded townspeople who had become wealthy when oil was found on their property. Happily he boarded the train with his father to start a new life.

He wore his smart, blue uniform as a cadet the first time on his fourteenth birthday, when he joined about fifty boys on the training ship *Mircea*, a 350-ton brig armed with two old Krupp guns and two Mitrailleuses, the French quick-firing gun that was a step in the development of the modern machine-gun.

But he found that the life of an officer cadet in the Romanian Navy was particularly hard and brutal—and promptly ran away. He got as far as Turkey, where he was arrested in Pera and returned by the Romanian Consul to Galatz. Here he was put in irons and imprisoned for four weeks in the ancient Fort Karubani in the Danube estuary opposite Galatz. Within a year he had run away again and one day in 1887 he arrived in Constantinople as a stowaway on the Turkish tramp *Kadi Keui*. As soon as the ship docked he slipped away from her and found himself among the dense traffic of the Uzun Charsi, the main artery of Constantinople. He followed the wide road into the native town until he reached the Grand Bazaar, a rabbit warren of small cobbled ways and alleys, all roofed with Oriental carpets.

A blue cap on his unruly hair, hands deep in the pockets of his creased and dirty naval tunic, he stared at the Aladdin's treasures exhibited on dirty wooden planks: gold and silver caskets, bracelets, brooches and diamond-studded belts. He listened to a bearded merchant fiercely haggling with a client over a price for a hammered-gold cup, calling Allah as his witness, in every living language, that the price offered by the infidel meant his utter ruin.

George walked slowly through the crowd of tourists surrounded by yelling urchins, crying for baksheesh, followed by packs of homeless, filthy dogs, through an incredible din, until he reached one exit of the market near the Mosque of Sultan Osman. Tired and hungry, he sat down on the steps of a house. All the earthly goods he possessed he wore on his body, he had no money and nothing to eat. Although it was only early afternoon he was worrying where he would sleep that night. Even so he could not rid his mind of the fantastic riches exhibited in the bazaar. More than ever he felt that the goods of this world were distributed very unfairly. (Many years later he told his second wife, Pauline, that the sight of the Grand Bazaar made him resolve there and then to get rich quickly, no matter how.)

His first three weeks in Constantinople got him no nearer his goal. He tried to attach himself to a gang of native boys but was savagely beaten up by them and told that he had better disappear into the European quarter on the opposite side of the Golden Horn.

In Galata were the European embassies and missions, the Christian churches, and the convents where he received food and shelter for seven nights. But what he needed most was money, and money he could not get. Finally he made up his mind. He walked over the Outer Bridge into the old native town and into the bazaar. Quite coolly he took a gold ring from one of the stands and escaped with it into the dense crowd while the merchant yelled, 'Thief!'

He ran all the way back to the European town. He had no qualms of conscience, it was an act of self-preservation and it had never occurred to him to try to find an honest way of making money!

The Greek jeweller in Pera who bought the ring did not ask any questions, but offered a scandalously low price and refused to bargain. He was a shrewd old man who knew his customers. George accepted; it was just enough to buy himself a second-hand suit and a decent meal in one of the many beer-gardens cum dance-halls patronized by sailors of half the races on earth.

According to George's memoirs, he sailed straight into an adventure with a Turkish official and a dancing girl and succeeded in stealing the official's money. Whether this was true or not, he still continued to go to the convents and charitable institutions in the European quarter to eat, and slept in the shelter for homeless at the Italian Mission.

However, he was now fairly decently dressed, in a grey suit, with drain-pipe trousers devoid of wrinkles, and a belted plaid coat. He spent his days mostly in the elegant Grande Rue, looking at the shops, lounging before one of the luxury hotels, or studying the enormous villas belonging to foreign embassies and rich Turkish officials.

One morning as he stood in front of the Hotel Bristol, he heard a commotion in the entrance hall. A small black poodle appeared in the doorway and marched slowly out, sniffed once or twice on the marble steps, then turned and walked down the street. Something caught its attention and suddenly it darted out into the road itself, barking loudly. A second later the door of the hotel was thrown wide and a woman in a fashionable, high-waisted lace dress, the long train sweeping after her, came running into the street. She stopped at the curb and called desperately: 'Chéri! Chéri! Come back at once!'

Chéri, however, was enjoying its freedom and was beginning to cross the road. Suddenly a clanging horse-tram approached. The woman dashed into the road between the carriages and rattling carts, followed by an excited group of hotel employees, while the brakes of the tram were applied with a piercing screech. George came to life. He jumped between the vehicles whose drivers shouted wildly at their rearing horses. He reached the little dog just before the hooves of the tram-horses would have crushed it. He gripped the small, struggling bundle firmly and jumped to safety on the opposite side of the Grande Rue.

The imposing figure of the be-fezzed commissionaire of the Hotel Bristol now succeeded in stopping the traffic and clearing a lane for the woman to cross over to George, who stood surrounded by a crowd of grooms and porters, loiterers and the inevitable beggars, babbling in a dozen languages.

The dog was snatched out of his arms by its agitated mistress, who cuddled it as she repeated over and over again: 'Mon pauvre, pauvre bijou.' Then, turning to George she said: 'You have saved my darling's life. How can I ever thank you?'

She had spoken in French, and George—thanks to Grandmother—answered in French. 'It was a pleasure, Madame.'

Madame looked appraisingly at the speaker. Though only fifteen, he was a tall young man, well built, with a healthy, tanned complexion and sleek black hair, now rather embarrassed and smiling stiffly.

'You must come to the hotel with me,' she said. 'I am certain my husband wishes to thank you as well,' and taking his arm she led a cavalcade of hotel employees and loafers back across the road, through the still-frozen traffic and the comments of the coachmen, which luckily neither she nor George could understand.

In the hall of the hotel George had his first glimpse of the world of luxury.

He followed Madame, who carried her darling firmly in her arms, past the desk of a hall porter dressed like an admiral, and up the sweeping marble staircase. She opened a door on the first floor and George found himself in a drawing-room, such as he had never seen before. At a desk under the high window sat an elderly man with a pointed grey beard, studying a pile of documents.

In a cascade of words Madame explained what had happened and suggested that George should stay for lunch. George had not eaten properly for two days, but he gave no sign of his hunger. He silently thanked his stars that his grandmother had taught him some kind of manners.

His host and hostess were friendly and sympathetic, and during the meal George learned that the man with the beard was a French diplomat, accredited to the Sublime Porte. The couple had rented a villa at Top Kaneh, the wealthy quarter of Galata, and had brought two personal servants from France.

During the meal Madame scarcely took her eyes from her guest. Gradually she turned the conversation to him and, natural raconteur and liar, he answered all questions put to him with consummate skill. There was no need to broadcast the fact that his father was a junior officer in an unimportant line regiment of a corrupt and bankrupt state; that he was a drunkard and a gambler and that the wolf was always at the door. He promoted him forthwith to Colonel in a crack regiment stationed in Bucharest and casually dropped into his tale names of important people in the capital whom he had heard mentioned in the officers' mess.

He did not disclose that his mother had died of a broken heart two years after his birth . . . no, *his* mother had died when he was born and his father had married again. He, George, had never forgiven him for that, for forgetting his beautiful mother so quickly. His fertile imagination built up the portrait of a strong-willed, well-educated boy, embarked upon a career as an officer in the Royal Romanian Navy, who could not bear seeing his mother's memory abused. It was a wonderful, romantic, heart-rending tale. By the time the meal was over George knew that he had impressed at least his hostess. While Monsieur returned to his work, Madame, visibly moved by his old-world loyalty to his dead mother, extracted the information that the boy had run away and was now a penniless deserter. He wanted to work at anything he could get to fulfil the dream of his life—to go to Paris, the fabulous city of light, wit and elegance. There was no doubt in George's mind that Madame liked him. Perhaps in the end she might give him a little money and a new suit of clothes, which, with the excellent meal, was not a bad payment for the rescue of one small dog.

He did not realize then how brilliant and convincing a storyteller he was; but Madame's heart was touched and she wanted to do something to help this romantic, wayward boy whom she found extremely likeable.

George was offered a job with Madame and Monsieur to supervize the native personnel at the villa near Top Kaneh. He accepted with alacrity and humble gratitude, and silently blessed the dead mother he could not even remember. A disapproving hall porter was called to provide the new member of the household with a room in the servants' quarters under the roof of the hotel, and thus George Manolesco stepped from the life of a loafer into the fairy-tale surroundings of high living. Card-sharping, poverty, hunger and fear of the law were a thing of the past, better forgotten. He was determined to make good.

Twenty years later, when George Manolesco, alias Prince Lahovary, was famous and had become the hero-crook of the century, he wrote his memoirs for a Romanian newspaper *Adeverul*. The horrified publishers cut from the manuscript the events that took place in the villa on Top Kaneh, which George had put down on paper with so much gusto and in great detail. It was not consideration for others, or special tact, or any feeling of decency that made the publishers decide to conceal young George's adventures in Pera. Nor were they worried that publication might offend the pure minds of Victorian maidens. As Romanians they did not believe in pure-minded maidens. Certain exalted quarters, however, suggested that the book would be banned and the publishers prosecuted if the tale of Top Kaneh were made public.

Manolesco, already on his way down from his pinnacle of fame, and always in need of money, made the best of the whole affair. He agreed, with the greatest apparent reluctance, to the suppression of his account of what he sadly called the happiest days of his life, on condition that the publishers would compensate him for his silence and add a large sum of money to the already-spent advance on the book.

The notes of the adventures in Pera, which George retained, were found after his death and kept by his adoring widow Pauline. They turned up again during the First World War, but then the Italians (for they were found in Milan) had other worries besides the affair between George Manolesco and the Comtesse de Boulogne. They were in the middle of a gigantic struggle for survival and not in the mood to rake up old stories. Today none of the people in the story remain alive. Therefore, here is the story of George's Pera adventure, as told by himself in the unpublished manuscript:

Whenever I think of Constantinople I always regard it as my lucky city. And invariably my thoughts are dominated by one of the most beautiful and vigorous women I have ever met: Valeria, Comtesse de Boulogne. I am not ashamed to confess that I dedicated a large candle to St. Francis of Assisi, the Saint of the animals, in *Notre-Dame de la Mission Française* in Pera, to bless and protect the awful little yapping dog she loved so much and which Providence elected me to save. I had the greatest affection for Madame and I soon knew that she, too, liked me, in a kind of motherly, considerate way.

Valeria de Boulogne was a stately woman with a ripe, Junoesque figure. She had full, naturally red lips and dark, burning eyes, in a lovely face in which, however, her surprisingly small and slightly *retroussé* nose seemed to be out of proportion. Its sauciness did not somehow fit her otherwise impressive appearance. Her hair was silky blue-black, and was expertly and artistically arranged every day by her French maid Marie, in the form of a regal crown, accentuating the paleness of her long face. When in the evening Marie loosened the *coiffure*, the hair fell down to her knees creating the impression of an angel with a black halo and deep dark wings. When I joined the household, she was about forty-two or forty-three years old, but looked ten years younger.

Her parents belonged to a wealthy family of silk spinners in Lyons and had married her to a career diplomat husband eighteen years her senior. It was a marriage of convenience and ambition, and none too happy. Monsieur le Comte was considerate and polite to Madame, but definitely not affectionate, being much too preoccupied with diplomatic intrigues and conferences.

In my boyish way I felt sorry for Valeria and showed her all my gratitude and affection whenever I found an opportunity. Often I purchased little presents, skilful native handiwork from the Turkish peddlars who came to the door, and gave them to her, neatly wrapped in coloured paper, and she always thanked me with a wonderful smile and a motherly kiss on the forehead.

Sometimes I was even jealous of Madame's poodle, who responded to her caresses by snapping at her fingers or making water on the priceless Persian carpets.

Madame trusted me. In her eyes I was an honest and unspoiled boy from a good family. So, great as was the temptation to improve my finances on the side, I did not touch anything which belonged to my benefactors. The villa was filled with wonderful treasures, stored in glass show-cases all over the ground floor: Asiatic snuff-boxes of gold and silver, studded with diamonds and rubies; watches from many countries; gold statuettes; and Monsieur's great collection of rare gold coins, only a small part of which could bring thousands of francs even if sold to one of the crooks in the Greek and Armenian quarter of the Port.

I was still young, but not imbecile enough to destroy my great chance for no reason.

The temperament which I possessed as a boy, however, became my downfall. I still had ideas of honour and was terribly proud of the name of Manolesco. I also had romantic ideas and illusions that the world was a good and friendly place, and that, as long as I behaved myself, the Saints were on my side. But . . .

It all began with a change in Valeria that brought me the

happiest time of my life. The day Monsieur received an urgent wire from Paris calling him back for consultations, Madame saw him off on the packetboat for Marseilles and returned to the villa. When I heard the carriage wheels crunching on the gravel of the drive I ran down to the entrance hall, as I always did, to help Madame out of her coat and ask for any special orders.

Jumping down the marble stairs I must have misjudged the distance, for I lost my balance and fell, knocking my knee against a column of the stairs. It was very painful and Madame called the Embassy doctor at once. He pronounced that it was nothing dangerous, only a painful bruise. It was nothing that could not be cured with rest.

I was sent up to my room and ordered to lie down. 'But, I was to go with Madame to the garden party at the Italian Consulate,' I stammered.

'Never mind,' she answered. 'I'll go alone. You rest your leg, my boy.'

I limped up the stairs to my little room, put a towel in water, stretched on a settee and cooled the swollen knee. A Turkish footman brought me some tea and sandwiches later in the afternoon, and I closed my eyes and dreamed of the future, wondering what it would have in store for me, making plans, and again blessing the luck that had made me meet my generous and lovable mistress.

Night fell and through the open window the distant noises of this brutally loud city died down. I could see the sky and the stars; and now and then I heard the clanging of the horse-trams in the main road. I undressed completely, for during the heat of the summer months I preferred to sleep in my natural state, slipped into bed and pulled the thin sheet over me.

The clock of the German Mission church struck midnight —I woke up because someone had entered my room. It was dark and I could not see very well, but I hoped it would be Marie, Madame's personal maid, a nice girl with a coquettish smile, blonde curls and no objections to a little cuddling and kissing. Perhaps she wanted to find out how I was after my accident. But it was not Marie. Getting used to the darkness,

I could now see in the half-open door a greyish-white shadow, much taller than Marie—it was Madame.

She stood in the door, listening, and then sensing that I was awake she came into the room and closed the door. She approached the bed.

She was wearing a light, embroidered *peignoir* and her long hair was falling down over her shoulders, framing her in a mysterious dark-blue shadow.

I lifted my head and stared at her.

'How is the leg, George?' she asked in her sweetest voice. 'The footman told me that the pain has gone but I have been worried.' She sat down on the edge of the bed, half facing me.

'Is it still swollen?' she asked, and began to stroke my forehead, which was now damp with embarrassment, for I was covered only by the thin linen sheet which I had now drawn up to my chin to hide my naked torso. Then she gently kissed my forehead, but I was so startled at this unconventional visit that my answers to her questions probably sounded brusque.

'I am all right,' I said, wriggling under the sheet, hoping she would go away.

But she only laughed. 'It seems to me,' she said in a curiously throaty voice, 'that you do not like to be kissed by me.'

'No . . . no . . .' I stuttered helplessly. 'On the contrary, Madame. . . .' I was absolutely at a loss as to how to behave. Madame was clearly enjoying my embarrassment and she bent down to kiss me again.

'Do you know, George,' she said, stroking my hair, 'I have had some curious dreams lately.'

'Dreams?' I said. 'What dreams?'

'Just dreams,' she said, 'dreams that included you . . . and me. I dreamed you are very fond of me, George.'

'I am fond of you, Madame,' I cried. 'More than I ever was of anyone in the world. I love you, Madame. . . .'

For answer she kissed me again. As she did so my downcast eyes could clearly see the shadowy cleft of the upper part of her breasts, for the moon was now flooding the room with silver. Madame smiled again as she noticed my glance, then she gently put out one hand and to my horror lowered the sheet so that my shoulders were bare. The natural modesty that is in most young boys flooded my cheeks with scarlet as she looked steadily down at me.

'You have nice white shoulders, George,' she said in a sort of husky purr I had never heard in any woman's voice before. 'It is a fine chest, too, a man's chest—but so hairless . . . you are but a hairless boy, my little George!' She was stroking my chest now with her right hand while her left hand held my wrists close clamped together and lying across my stomach. Slowly, languorously almost, she slid the sheet down to my navel. To my stupefaction, she bent down once more and kissed me there and, with her face still close to my body, moved the sheet farther down, impatiently pushing my protesting hands away. Then she glanced back to my burning face and said: 'Not so hairless, my little George, not such a little boy perhaps as all that. But we must look at your injured leg!'

She whipped the sheet right off now and laid her hand on my still slightly swollen knee, sliding her fingers up and down my thigh and looking me straight between the eyes as she did so. I was so completely astonished and discomfited by now that any natural urges I might have had, such as with Marie, deserted me and I was indeed but a little boy under her deep, glowing eyes.

Her hand had strayed far away from my knee now. As her questing fingers felt the lack of response in me she suddenly stood up, laughing very softly. She undid the ribbons fastening the *peignoir* and dropped it to the floor. She was wearing an almost transparent silk night-dress through which I could see not only every curve of her body but its changing hues, the shoulders and chest tanned from her sunbathing in isolation on the Embassy roof, the whiter globes of her breasts—the first I had ever seen. They seemed to me very large. Down her body my eyes followed every curve of her, every shadow.

'Perhaps, little George, we can find out if you are a boy or a man,' she said and laid herself down on the bed beside me as I moved over, almost automatically, to make room for her. She kissed me again, but on the lips this time, then her tongue found its way between my teeth and I experienced for the first time the perfection of a mature woman's kisses. Marie's were like ice compared with this voluptuous creature who had now taken my hand and fastened it over her breast and was gently but persistently stroking herself—with my hand.

No human could resist it; I felt the signs of fast awakening desire and so did Madame's free hand. I tried to slide the strap of her night-dress down to kiss her shoulder—I had not dared to return her kiss on the lips.

'Silly, inexperienced boy,' she laughed, but not unkindly. 'It will not come down that way. You will have to take it off—from the bottom. I will not help you, you must disrobe your first woman for yourself—it *is* your first is it not?'

'Yes, Madame,' I found the strength to say, then I was kneeling by the side of the bed both hands on the lower hem of her night-dress, staring at her face. Her eyes now looked damply brilliant, like the stars themselves, her lips were slightly parted and her bosom was heaving slowly. I dropped my eyes to my hands and slowly, and as caressingly I realized afterwards as any experienced lover, I slid her night-dress up. When it had reached her neck, she sat up and swept it over her head throwing it to the floor with an imperious movement. For a moment or two she sat there, immobile, gloriously beautiful in the moonlight; as I stood up she stretched out her arms and pulled me to her, sinking her lips on to my body. Truly now I was no longer a boy but a man.

For hours through that night Madame masterfully and passionately taught me the science and joys of physical love; that she was sex-starved I now realize; her elderly husband just did not appreciate what he had in her!

Towards dawn she left me.

* * *

Once started, this affair with Valeria lasted more than three months and with ever-growing passion. Once she said to me: 'You know, George, for your eighteen years you are very intelligent. I am certain you will be a great man one day.' I did not correct her by telling her that I had just passed my sixteenth birthday, but I replied: 'You mean a great *gentleman*!'

Though we tried to hide our feelings if others were present, in the narrow confines of the villa it was bound to be noticed that Valeria and I were in love. Not that it made much difference, for Valeria did not care what others thought. When I mentioned to her that other ladies of her circle regarded me with special curiosity, and were more friendly to me than they used to be, she just shrugged.

'They are just envying me for having you as my pet!' she answered laughing. 'Don't take any notice. They are jealous bitches and would like to take you away from me.'

It was a peculiar experience to be such a centre of female attention, but I pretended not to notice it. I lived in the clouds, deeply in love. I hoped only that this affair would go on for ever and ever.

But it came to an abrupt end one night, and my entire world fell in shambles. Valeria had been invited to a reception at one of the foreign missions and I went down to the basement of the villa to have dinner with my colleagues in the servants' hall. For, officially, I was still a servant in the Count's household and fulfilled my duties as such conscientiously every day. Among the half-dozen servants in the house and now assembled for a meal, was Etienne, the second valet to Monsieur le Comte. We disliked each other thoroughly. Etienne always tried to provoke me but generally I ignored him, which only made him the more vicious. To make things worse he had started an affair with Marie since I had completely neglected her, and from his sneering remarks I concluded that Marie must have told him about Valeria and me.

Etienne was a small wiry Frenchman from Provence and about twenty-eight years old. He always called me 'my boy'. Tonight the party was in a gay mood. Monsieur was still away in France, and Madame would not be back at the villa before midnight. They had acquired a few bottles of wine from the master's cellar and cook had prepared an excellent dinner.

'George!' called Etienne when I entered the room, and raised his glass. 'Come over here and sit down. And let me drink to your very good health . . . *and to our loves!*'

I ignored him and took a chair. He grinned maliciously. 'You have made another conquest, my boy!' he announced. 'The honorable Baroness Felicia de Stratonia from the Italian Embassy. Did you know that she has asked Madame about you?'

I looked at him but did not answer.

'She has had an eye on you for a long time,' he laughed. 'I am not surprised. A wonderful boy like you. And so strong . . . hein? Now, she has asked Madame whether she could borrow you for a few weeks.'

'Borrow me?' I asked in spite of myself. 'What for?'

He shrugged. 'How should I know?' he answered, grinning. 'Maybe to count marbles,' an answer that produced a howl of laughter from the others.

'During the tea-party Madame gave last week,' he said, 'I saw her looking at you through her lorgnettes for at least twenty minutes.'

I blushed under the renewed burst of laughter. 'Look!' cried Etienne. 'He can still blush. The innocent kid.' He took a fork from the table and raised it to his eyes like a lorgnette, clicked his tongue to indicate the snapping opening of the mechanism, and regarded me with half-closed eyes, nodding his head and licking his lips. 'A wonderful boy,' he uttered in a falsetto voice. 'Indeed, a wonderful animal . . . !'

'Shut up, you bastard!' I shouted.

Etienne was now in full swing. He dropped the fork back on the table and said with the intimate confidence of the half-drunk: 'She is a beauty, the Baroness is. A real peach! The beautiful Felicia. And what a temperament! Honestly, I would prefer her to Madame.'

I slammed my fist on the table. 'What do you mean?' I shouted. 'Leave Madame out of this!'

Etienne laughed loudly. 'Once the gallant, always the

gallant, the boy with the fatal charm no one can resist, the pet of the ladies of Pera. Bless him!' And with the vile imagination of the sordid little man that he was, Etienne described in words that left not the slightest doubt what duties would be expected from me by the Baroness. He concluded with a nasty smile and a deep bow: 'With Madame's permission, naturally.'

For a second or two I was speechless. Then the whole implications of Etienne's allegations dawned on me.

'You dirty swine!' I shouted and gripped a crystal carafe of wine on the table. I swung it wildly at the grinning valet, who fell to the floor with a loud cry and lay moaning with pain, while the carafe smashed into smithereens on the tiled floor. None of the servants had moved. Without waiting to see what harm I had done to my torturer, I ran out of the room followed by a burst of applause from the servants.

*　　*　　*

I had made up my mind not to mention the unpleasant scene in the servants' quarters to Valeria. I did not believe Etienne's words, knowing his dirty, malicious mind. Then something happened which recalled the events in a completely new light.

Three days after the brawl, I was called by a footman to Madame's drawing-room.

'George,' she said, friendly as always, 'I have received a telegram from Monsieur. He asks me to meet him in Rome on his way back. I cannot take you with me, my pet, much as I would have loved to. I am only taking Marie.'

I must have shown my disappointment, for she laughed and patted my hand. 'It is only for four weeks, my love,' she said. 'I am to close the house in the meantime and cook and Etienne are taking a holiday while I am away. The butler is being taken over for the duration by the First Secretary of the Embassy, so there remains only you.

'I can stay at the villa and take care of things,' I said eagerly.

'Very good of you, my boy,' she answered tenderly. 'But

the house is being closed down. There is another alternative, however, which has just cropped up. Would you like to help out at the summer house of one of my friends? Until I return?'

A feeling of suspicion seized me and I pulled my hand away. 'Who?' I asked shortly.

'The Italian Ambassador.'

'Baroness Stratonia?' I nearly shouted.

She nodded, visibly taken aback. 'What is wrong with the Baroness?' she asked coldly.

I did not answer for quite a time. The scene in the servants' quarters appeared before my eyes. Etienne had been right!

I tried to persuade myself that it was impossible that Valeria could give me away like a piece of jewellery or an animal. Without mincing words I told her of the scene in the servants' quarters. I reminded her that she, herself, had said that the women were all bitches, and I told her that I was too proud to be given away like a prime bull.

Valeria heard me out silently, but whitening with fury. At the end she stood up, a majestic figure of a woman, trembling with the effort to control herself. 'George,' she said icily, 'you are a dirty little boy. How I ever believed your comedy of devotion and tenderness! How could I ever trust you, who so eagerly believes the tales of a guttersnipe. Get out! Get out at once! Pack your things and go . . . into the gutter, where I picked you up!'

She clutched her silver handbag and swung it, slapping me right and left across the face, leaving two hot burning marks and the blood trickling from my nose.

'Out!' she said and threw a coin at me. 'Here is your wage!'

It was a Louis d'Or.

I ran from the room, clutching the gold coin, half out of my senses. To kick me out of the house like a dog. Because I had said what perhaps was the truth after all? Because she was a bitch after all? No one could treat George Manolesco like that, not even the beautiful Valeria de Boulogne. I looked around. There were the glass cases with Monsieur le Comte's precious collection. There was my revenge for George Manolesco's humiliation, the means both to teach her a lesson and help me in my predicament. A Louis d'Or for my services? No, the services of George Manolesco were not that cheap.

Calmly I choose six gold boxes studded with diamonds from one of the cases, put them in my pocket, fetched my luggage and left the house. The proceeds from the boxes would enable me to leave Constantinople as a gentleman.

I did not care a damn what Valeria would do. I was convinced she would not raise the alarm when the loss of the boxes was discovered. She would find an explanation for their disappearance. And if not, just too bad! I sold the boxes right away in the harbour quarter and booked a first-class ticket on the steamer of the Messagères Maritimes to Athens.

When at four in the afternoon the boat steamed out of the Golden Horn and into the Bosphorus, I stood at the porthole of my cabin on the upper-deck and looked out at the rows of golden-roofed mosques and steep minarets slowly gliding by. When the boat turned around after having passed the Outer Bridge, I saw for the last time Top Kaneh and the white-walled villas of the Diplomatic Corps. My feelings of hatred and fury had left me, and a great regret came over me when I recognized the dark cypresses, the red roof and the white walls of the villa on the hill-side. How foolish and childish I had been! I still regret my actions today, for they made me lose my first and only great love.

hapter 2

George arrived in the big Greek port of Piraeus with two ten-franc pieces of gold in his pocket, and an elegant pigskin suitcase, the former property of Monsieur le Comte de Boulogne. Instead of taking 'Greece's pride', the new railway to Athens, he travelled in grand style and hired a carriage for the two-hour ride. Only the very best, the most expensive hotel in the capital, was good enough for him. Having heard much at Top Kaneh about the luxury of the Hôtel des Étrangers, he walked up to their reception desk and asked them to pay off his carriage! Knowing that a traveller arriving with but one piece of baggage, in an era when wealthy travellers took dozens of trunks and cases on their journeys, would be viewed with reserve if not suspicion, he casually mentioned that he had been recommended the hotel by the Baroness Stratonia. For good measure he produced one of the visiting cards which the Comtesse de Boulogne had had printed for him:

M. GEORGES MANOLESCO
Mission Française
Top Kaneh, Pera

He mentioned that the rest of his luggage would follow, gave the head-porter one of his two gold pieces, and was allocated a luxurious room in the newly opened annex of the famous hotel. It held a gigantic four-poster bed; the white marble floor was covered with Oriental rugs; and in a small cabinet stood a china wash-basin, pitcher and glasses.

Glass doors led to a small balcony with two wicker chairs. From here he could look down on the Place de la Constitution, the hub of Athens, its social centre and its meeting-place. The pavements were crowded with rows of coffee tables; the horse-trams had their terminal just across the square. A never-ending throng of leisurely strollers listened to soft music from the fiddlers on the coffee-house terrace of Yannopoulus. Dozens of carriages drove in a circle round the square, with the Acropolis high above as if put there by a good stage designer with a sense for background.

George hardly bothered to look at the scene. He had already discovered in his room a notice in a small gilt frame which, in three languages, informed the hotel's guests of the price of the room—fifteen francs a day, to be paid in gold and upon presentation of the account every fifth day. The price did include, however, breakfast and table d'hôte lunch and dinner.

As at this moment he had not the faintest idea how he would pay any bill, George thought he might just as well go and have dinner. He enjoyed an excellent meal with a glass of resinous Greek wine. More than ever was he determined to stay at the hotel, for when he had looked through the register of guests he discovered that he was living under the same roof as two ambassadors, three English peers, and a mixed collection of artists and scientists, some with valets and grooms, visiting the show-places of ancient Greece. It was definitely the right company for George Manolesco.

In later years George always said that his stay in Greece was his real apprenticeship in the noble crafts of thief and con-man. For here he developed an astonishing egotism, brazenness and cunning, and came to regard nothing as impossible for him.

In those days travel in Greece was difficult. Foreign visitors were very wealthy people who could afford to penetrate the interior in private carriages or on horseback and hire guides to take them through a still wild country. Such journeys to the interior meant travelling light, and all heavy and bulky luggage was kept behind in the principal hotels of Athens. This was George's chance. On every floor of the

Hôtel des Étrangers was a baggage room. On his very first evening George discovered that the one on his own floor was unlocked and held rich and easy booty. Most of the luggage was not even locked. Nearly all the big trunks were secured only by leather straps or even by strong cord, which simplified matters greatly.

Late that night he went to work. He found jewellery and banknotes in many of the trunks and cases, useless to the travellers to the interior. Even banknotes were eyed with suspicion in the capital where gold was the legal tender, and even that was always tested for fear of counterfeiting.

That first night George lifted about £2,000 from the Hôtel des Étrangers. Telling the story years afterwards, he always rejected the suggestion that he was just lucky. 'Certainly,' he would say, 'luck played a certain role, it has to. But the main element in my success was the atmosphere at the hotel. I learned the basic lesson in Athens that people lulled by the gracious comfort of a well-run hotel, become careless. And if at home they are accustomed to the services of a personal valet, and while travelling must look after themselves, they are absolutely helpless and completely at a loss as to what to do with the heaps of luggage they call their own! Often they do not even know what they carry in their cases and trunks.'

George was never suspected at the Hôtel des Étrangers. In those days no first-class hotel would ever admit that property had disappeared within its sacred walls. Admittedly there were hundreds of thieves in Athens, but none would dare enter the hotel! As for a guest robbing fellow guests, it was never even considered!

George sold the jewellery in the Turkish quarter under the hill of the Acropolis, the banknotes he brought to the Street of Money Changers, the rue Aeolus, where he demanded gold drachmae in exchange for foreign paper-money, and called the changers 'vultures' and 'crooks' when, almost weeping with sincerity, they offered him rates that were, said George, mere tips.

The next night George visited the Hotel Britannia, opposite the Étrangers, but here he was nearly caught by a watchful valet and decided to relax for a time. For two weeks he lived like a millionaire. On the coffee terrace of the hotel he met an employee of the Austrian Embassy who introduced him to the night life of Athens. Soon the dancing girls in the *cafés chantants* in the rue Hermes competed for the favours of the flamboyant guest who always drank champagne and listened generously to any hard-luck story; gipsies in restaurants played their sad tunes for him alone, rewarded by champagne and gold pieces. George enjoyed wine, song . . . and women. He rarely returned to his hotel room before daybreak.

In a fortnight George, with the assistance of Ilonka, a ravishing Hungarian cabaret singer, was left with but three pieces of gold. He thought of going into the rue Aeolus and making a quick grab at the wooden stands of the money changers. But as there were always several National Guards walking through the street, he dropped the idea. From money changers his thoughts went naturally to bankers proper: certainly a bank was the best place to provide George Manolesco with cash. Into the Ionian Bank, the biggest in Greece, he walked and he sent his card in to the Director.

George was received by an Englishman '. . . as long as a beanstalk, and cold as a fish, and very impolite'. In no time he was out of the bank. He tried his luck at two others, but again without success. Deep in thought he strolled towards his hotel by way of the rue Aeolus, where, behind the rows of wooden stands, he saw a painted wooden board on a house which announced in Greek, French and English:

FRAISSINET & CIE., S.A.
ALL BANKING BUSINESS TRANSACTED

George remembered the name Fraissinet as that of a French shipping line; most probably the owner of this uninviting establishment would be a relation. On the spur of the moment he stepped into the cave-like office where, behind a dusty desk, sat a young, bored and sleepy Greek.

The Manolesco visiting card produced from the back room a huge man with a flaming red beard, wearing a rumpled white linen suit of doubtful cleanliness and a dirty pith helmet pushed back on his unruly red head. He ushered the young visitor into his private office and offered him a rickety chair. Sitting behind his own desk the red-haired giant seemed to smell business. In a second or two he had sized up his visitor with shrewd eyes, and begun a long rigmarole about the importance of his banking house. Only once did George interrupt him, to mention casually that he had been told about Monsieur Fraissinet by the Baroness de Stratonia. This produced a pleasant smile from Monsieur Fraissinet; then the banker asked: 'What can I do for you?'

'I want to open an account,' answered George, who had learned a few things during his previous futile visits to banks, and now knew that to open an account was the key to the heart of a banker.

Monsieur Fraissinet reacted properly and beamed. 'Très bien, Monsieur,' he said. 'How much?'

George smiled back. 'That,' he said, 'depends entirely on how much credit you can allow me!'

'I do not understand you,' said the banker.

'It is quite simple,' answered George, who was beginning to enjoy himself thoroughly. He went on in his most charming manner: 'I want some credit from you.'

'Credit?' said Monsieur Fraissinet, much taken aback. 'You want to borrow money from me?'

'Precisely,' said Manolesco.

Monsieur Fraissinet looked at him sternly. 'I am not a money lender.'

'I know, Monsieur,' was George's answer. 'You are a banker. And besides it is not a huge sum of money I want. Just enough to tide me over until my letter of credit arrives. Which I then would naturally draw on your bank.'

Monsieur Fraissinet did not answer. Instead he picked up George's visiting card and studied it silently.

'Well,' he said after a while, 'have you any securities, or do you know a person of standing in Athens to recommend you?'

'I am staying at the Hôtel des Étrangers,' answered Manolesco. 'You can inquire there.'

'Anyone can stay at a hotel.'

'If he pays the bill,' nodded Manolesco.

'Naturally,' agreed Monsieur Fraissinet. 'But still it is not a recommendation.'

'I always pay my bills,' said Manolesco gravely.

'No doubt you do,' said Monsieur Fraissinet. 'But you want to borrow money from me—probably to pay your hotel bill. I do not know you. You have no securities and nobody in this town to give you a recommendation. How can I have sufficient confidence in you to lend you money?'

'Monsieur,' said Manolesco with great dignity, 'I do not know you either, and yet I have the confidence in you to come to you for money, and what is more, the confidence that you have got it. Why should you not have enough confidence in me to lend it to me?'

For a second or two Monsieur Fraissinet sat speechless, staring at George. Then his Gallic sense of humour won and he exploded into laughter. 'C'est formidable!' he cried. 'This is unique! I have the feeling you have nearly convinced me that to borrow money is merely a matter of mutual confidence, not of substance or standing. How much do you want?'

'Five hundred drachmae,' answered George, cool and businesslike, and he added: 'In gold.'

Another burst of laughter from Monsieur Fraissinet. 'You are an enterprising young man,' he said, wiping tears from his eyes. 'I like your unbelievable cheek. And I always adore a good joke, and this is definitely an excellent joke; anyway good enough to be rewarded. I will follow your advice and have confidence in you, so as not to disappoint the confidence you have in me. I will give you forty drachmae as a loan. If and when you come back within three weeks and repay me, you can have another loan.'

So far this was a great success for George's personality, but by no means enough to pay his hotel bill. With regret he decided to drop Ilonka.

Next he went to the hotel manager, tinkling his gold in his pocket, to tell him that his letter of credit was delayed. As George had paid his account up to the week before, the manager reluctantly agreed to wait. But when the next bill—for fifteen days—was presented, George was all but penniless. He was now quite notorious in Athens, which hampered his movements and prohibited any quick smash-and-grab jobs. A second expedition to the baggage rooms of the Hôtel des Étrangers nearly ended in catastrophe, so George decided to go to the Romanian Legation, just opened in Athens, to ask for help. Dressed in his perfectly-pressed linen suit, panama hat at a rakish angle, gleaming brown leather boots and with a yellow cane, he first went to a second-hand dealer in the Turkish quarter. He suggested that the trader should take his pigskin case and its contents and in return pay his hotel bill. He took the man to his hotel room and after much bargaining sold the suits which he had had made in Athens together with all his other belongings for enough to pay the greater part of his bill. Then he went to the nearby Hôtel Royale where the Romanian Legation had taken up temporary quarters.

The Counsellor of the Legation eyed his visitor with suspicion. It was not every day that a caller dressed like nobility asked for financial help. Politely George was told that the Legation had no money. There were scores of Romanian citizens about, some of them near starvation, and the Legation was unable to assist them. Usually they were given a voucher for one free meal in a small Romanian-owned restaurant in the Old Town. But no money.

It was frustrating and depressing. No argument from George changed the Counsellor's attitude. He had heard tales of woe far too often before. George burst out in rage. He told the official frankly what he thought of him and of the entire State of Romania, and of its Civil Service, and he used the foulest language he could remember from his days aboard the Royal Romanian Navy training ship *Mircea*. At first the Counsellor did not say a word, but when George suggested that the diplomat probably had more fathers than his mother could remember, it was too much; George was thrown out of the Legation without even a voucher for a meal.

He did not dare return to the Hôtel des Étrangers, where

by now they would have discovered the disappearance of his luggage. He cursed himself for having paid even a part of his hotel bill. He had some silver in his pocket, enough to buy a meal in a small restaurant. He was burning for revenge. He wanted to show this arrogant Counsellor that no one could treat George Manolesco like that! After his meal he was strolling through the streets, deep in thought, when in the rue de Stade he saw the window of a locksmith who advertised the repair of cashboxes, travellers' trunks and pistols. An idea struck him. He entered the shop, run by Herr Peter Moser, a Viennese with a snow-white beard. In his best German, George asked to see pistols. The old gentleman eagerly produced his stock, and George carefully scrutinized the weapons, eventually choosing one for fifteen drachmae.

'Send it to the Hôtel des Étrangers,' George ordered. 'The porter will pay you.'

While the shopkeeper wrote down the instructions on a high desk in a corner of his shop, George put another pistol in his pocket. The ammunition was in a small cardboard box tied to it.

George went straight to the Hôtel Royale. In the men's room he loaded the pistol and then marched upstairs to the rooms of the Legation. But it was now the hour of siesta and the Legation was closed. A note on the door, however, indicated that the Counsellor lived in the hotel, so George went to the door of his suite; this was opened almost immediately by the Counsellor himself, who recognized George at once. Before the enraged diplomat could slam the door shut, George rushed in and shouted at the top of his voice: 'Will you help me to get home again, and give me a ticket to Romania?'

The Counsellor tried to stop him but George only pushed him aside and repeated his question in an even louder voice.

'No!' shouted the Counsellor furiously. 'Get out of here, before I hand you over to the police!'

George produced his gun. 'You refuse to help me?' he shouted. Then dropping to an impressively calm voice, he went on: 'I will kill myself before your eyes, and my blood will be upon you!'

'Put the pistol down!' the horrified diplomat cried.

'Go away, you bastard,' said George and pushed him aside. He walked over to stand in front of a long wall mirror, and then, choosing his left arm where a bullet would create the least inconvenience, he pulled the trigger.

The report cracked sharply through the silence of the siesta. George fell to the carpet, the smell of cordite filled the room, doors flew open all along the corridor. As for the Counsellor—he fainted.

Hotel employees rushed to the suite, collected the body on the carpet, put it into a carriage and rushed it to the only casualty-centre in Athens, a hospital for the dying, run by French nuns, and called the Hospital of the Orphans and Foundlings.

The young and inexperienced doctors on duty during the siesta hour were presented with an unusual problem—the patient pointed at his arm with which there was nothing wrong, while a bullet was embedded in his left thigh! George was not a very good marksman. The doctors were used to broken heads, even stab wounds, but bullet-wounds were rare to them. They probed to remove the bullet but only induced heavy bleeding, so George was bandaged and carried into the one and only ward. There he was dumped on one of the hundred narrow cots with thin straw mattresses, and a nun put ice bags on his head and on his swelling leg. The large ward was filled with horrible sounds of weeping and groaning, shouting and raving, and with nauseating smells. George just wanted to die. The pain became unbearable and he fell into unconsciousness.

It was dark when he came to. The ward was dimly illuminated by oil lamps, and he heard two men murmuring in French. Standing by his cot was a man in a tight-waisted dark overcoat with a small fur collar, cut in the latest English fashion. He had a grey top hat and carried a thick ebony cane. On his nose were pince-nez, secured by a wide black ribbon round his neck. George stared at the man—the most elegant he had ever seen. A small group of other well-dressed men listened attentively to his words and half a dozen nuns fussed around. This was the famous Dr. Pretenderi, personal physician to King George of the Hellenes; a great showman, but also an excellent doctor. A screen was put around George's cot, nuns held up lamps to form a circle of light, and a small table with instruments and hot water was brought in by the young doctors. Dr. Pretenderi took off his top hat and gave it to a nun to hold. He took off his wonderfully-cut top coat and long grey morning coat. While he turned up his shirt-sleeves and washed his hands, a student bound a leather apron round his waist, and in deadly silence, without anaesthetic, he started to remove the bullet from the leg.

'Two old nuns held me down,' recalled George. 'But I did not feel any pain . . . the leg was so swollen. I just fainted.'

It took the doctor about ten minutes to remove the bullet.

To the surprise of the medical staff of the hospital, George was still alive two days later and by the end of September he was so much better that he could sit up in his cot. Then, one evening, the matron rushed into the ward and announced: 'Her Majesty the Queen is here!'

There she was, already entering the ward, accompanied only by a lady-in-waiting and a secretary. A tall, beautiful woman, she smiled at the patients and nuns as she moved from one cot to the other.

The Queen stopped at George's cot and regarded him thoughtfully. Dr. Pretenderi had told her of the curious case of the young man with the wounded leg who did not fit at all into his present morbid surroundings. He was, she thought, good-looking, despite his deathly white face. She addressed him in a hard, foreign French with a strong Slav accent, for she had been born Princess Olga Constantinowna, the daughter of a Russian Grand Duke.

Next day George was transferred to a private room. After a few days the Queen returned to talk with her protégé. Again, Manolesco, with all the charm he could muster, repeated the long, sad story he had told Valeria in Pera, but with one variation. This time he made his father a nobleman, and involved his family in an old and deadly feud with the family of the Counsellor of the Romanian Legation! Queen Olga was deeply shocked and felt sorry for him. For she knew well enough that such feuds were nothing extraordinary in the strange lands of the Balkans, and that they were fought with venom and malice, with nothing barred, not even murder. She felt great pity for the good-looking boy, who reminded her so much of her cousin in St. Petersburg, and summoned the Counsellor of the Legation to the Palace to persuade him that his behaviour was unworthy of a diplomat.

The Counsellor found it impossible to confess to the Queen that the finances of the Kingdom of Romania were such that no money had been sent to the Legation in Athens—the cash had probably found its way into the pockets of civil servants during transit. Although he did not quite understand Queen Olga's references to feuds and family quarrels, he did not dare to argue with her, and for the honour of his country promised to forget everything that had happened and to give young Manolesco a ticket home; he did not add that he would have to pay the cost out of his own pocket.

Then, friendly relations between Greece and Romania unruffled, Queen Olga visited George again to tell him the news. She sent him a complete new outfit of clothes, since one leg of the trousers of his only suit had been cut off and the rest had disappeared. On the day of his release from hospital, a carriage sent by the Queen took him to the rue Hermes, where he was boarded with two former Russian servants of the Queen. An invitation to the Palace followed, and George, dressed in his new clothes, had tea with Her Majesty. The more she talked with this charming boy, the more she liked him, and when on taking his leave he gallantly kissed her hand, he had won not only her sympathy but also her heart.

'Before you leave Athens,' said Queen Olga as if a sudden thought had struck her, 'you should see some of the famous sights of this beautiful country.'

George bowed. 'Your Majesty,' he answered, 'I came here to do just that, to visit the places where history was made. But I did not have the opportunity after I was robbed of my possessions. . . .' His voice was sad and disappointed.

Queen Olga nodded. 'I do not want you to go from here with ill-feeling for my great country and with the thought that we were inhospitable. You shall visit some of the places you wanted to see. In the morning my own carriage will take you.'

The next day a footman called to escort George to the Palace where, waiting at the gates, stood Her Majesty's carriage, with Queen Olga herself sitting smiling at him. 'I thought it might give you more pleasure if I were to show you round.'

For several days the Queen's carriage was seen in the hills around the capital with Her Majesty eagerly explaining to her young companion the buildings and ruins they passed. George did not care a damn about the glory that was Greece, but he thoroughly enjoyed being driven around in the royal carriage with a genuine Queen by his side, cheered by the population and saluted by every man in uniform. After all, the agony had been worth while; he was again on top of the world.

At last a messenger from the Romanian Legation handed George a second-class ticket to Constanta, via Constantinople and Burgas, on a French passenger boat leaving the next day. He also gave him a little money for basic expenses. George used most of this to present himself at the Palace with a huge bunch of flowers. Queen Olga kissed him on the cheek and wished him good fortune, adding: 'I will send my carriage to take you to the harbour. Let us hope I will see you again in better and happier circumstances.'

Thus George Manolesco left the Greek capital in even greater style than he had entered it. All along the route to the port of Piraeus, National Guards stood to attention, peasants bowed deeply to the lone passenger in the well-known royal carriage, and George proudly returned the greetings with an indolent wave of his hand. On the main square of Piraeus he dismissed the carriage and quickly disappeared into one of the narrow side-streets. He had not the slightest intention of returning to Romania where he most certainly would again have been put in chains as a deserter. He sold his ticket to a ship's-broker and bought himself one to France—in the opposite direction. All he could afford was a steerage passage, but it was on a boat of the Fraissinet Line, a name for which George understandably had a great fondness. He regarded it as a good omen.

Late that night he boarded a tender that took him out to the ship, at last on the way to his dream city, Paris. He was in the best of spirits, full of plans for a great and wonderful future, and anticipating five days of carefree laziness aboard the steamer.

However, he was due for a great shock.

With about a dozen passengers for the steerage, he had to assemble in front of the aft companion-way. Ten bearded *matelots* formed a kind of ring around the small group until the door of the companion-way was opened to allow the passengers to enter. A steep, dark stairway led far down to the lowest hold of the boat. Here, yelling, singing, and a most revolting smell assailed the arriving passengers. George stopped, horrified, reluctant to enter this hell-hole, but an energetic push from a guard behind him sent him stumbling down the stairway to crash into a throng of black-coated, bearded Jews from Russia about to say their evening prayers. Their singing stopped, and gently and smilingly they helped George to his feet. They had just escaped another Cossack pogrom and were far too thankful for their freedom and still too frightened of the strange new world to resent any rudeness towards them.

George moved away, straight into the arms of an Armenian refugee from Turkey, wearing an Astrakhan coat despite the torrid heat, over which was a gold chain and golden armlets. In the dim light of a few oil lamps, whose fumes added to the reeking atmosphere, he finally found a small vacant corner where he could sit on the bare floor and recover from the shock. Slant-eyed Greeks watched him, on the look-out for something to steal. Then up came a small Bulgarian, who asked George, in a mixture of most of the Balkan languages, what he was doing here. Gasping for air, George answered him: 'Where can I go on deck? I am ill . . . I am about to die. . . .'

Laughter broke out on all sides. 'No go deck,' he was informed. 'Big door always be shut. Nix opened . . . until Marseilles.'

Five days and five nights in this inferno was out of the question for George. Furious, he forced a way through the circle that had formed around him and ran up the stairway to the locked door to the deck. He hammered it with hands and feet until it was opened by a seaman, and spitting and spluttering with rage, George yelled that he would die—yes, die!—unless he got air. The seaman was used to all sorts of protests in all sorts of languages from the human cargo in the steerage, but a complaint of lack of fresh air, delivered in faultless French, was something new.

Looking at the young man, he decided he must have got into the steerage by mistake, and escorted George to the deck. George rushed out into the air and promptly fell heavily on the slippery planks. Unconscious, he was carried to the ship's sick bay. Here the doctor kept him, not knowing exactly what was wrong with him; it could be anything on such voyages, and sick steerage passengers were definitely not to the liking of the company. They had brought too many epidemics into France, and if anyone died during the journey it meant a long delay in port and extra feeding for all the other passengers—especially if plague was the cause. When the ship berthed at Marseilles, George was bundled on to a stretcher and carried into the port hospital, but nothing wrong was found. He was now rested, and the medical authorities allowed his release after forty-eight hours. As the little Greek silver money he had did not find a willing market, he joined the army of beachcombers on the quaysides, sleeping under bridges or in warehouse doorways. His food came from the galleys aboard the ships anchored along the quays. His new friends among the riff-raff of the port warned him of the unfeeling wickedness of the French police, ever on the look-out for such as George, attracted from all over the Mediterranean to the wealthy port, the gateway to France. At first George was careful enough to avoid an encounter with the police, he did not even try to steal. He tried to work honestly at plastering posters on walls, but was chased by the police, because they were banned political posters. Now and then he succeeded in 'finding' odd saleable articles aboard the ships on which he had had meals.

Whenever he could he went into the new town of Marseilles, away from the sordid area of poverty and crime in the Old Port, to listen to the military bands playing to the crowds in the elegant rue de Meilhan.

After his early taste of high life, after mingling with countesses, baronesses and a Queen, this was by no means the life George had visualized. But it was becoming more and more difficult to get back to a life of luxury, for with every day that passed, he lost more of his elegance, his clothes were dirty, torn and creased, his shoes were cracking, and his hair uncut and unruly.

His instinct for money was, however, as keen as before, and soon he hit on a wonderful idea to make some without lifting a finger. By day, he had noticed dozens of street musicians who strolled from café to café, collecting money for pretty ghastly music. One night as they lay huddled together in the doorway they shared, George prodded his sleepy companion, the leader of a street band, and made his suggestion.

The next day the little band, trumpets and pipes in hand, marched to the centre of the New Town and stopped in front of the crowded terrace of the Grand Café, the liveliest place of Marseilles, where the Cannebière and rue Noailles met. George and the leader entered the glassed-in terrace and went from table to table.

'Monsieur,' said George to the occupant of each. 'You would like to hear some music, hein?' Seeing the horrified faces of the guests, he added smiling: 'Give me a few sous . . . and *we do not play!*'

Without any work the little band made more money than ever before. For two days all went well, with the proceeds divided each night. But on the third day there was no band.

'They had evaporated,' said George. 'There was no honour among thieves in Marseilles, no one expected that in a rotten port like this, with the exception of me, innocent George Manolesco. But I was cured.'

A morning or two later he strolled through the Old Town on the way to a free breakfast in a convent, when he heard loud voices from a small bistro. *The voices spoke in Romanian.* Sitting at a table were three men: a ship's captain in a gold-braided uniform, a little bird-like man in shabby clothes, and a well-groomed fat man, not much older than George, smoking a big cigar and smiling at the heated words from his smaller companion.

George went up to the table and addressed the fat man in Romanian. The conversation stopped.

'I am hungry,' said George simply. 'Could a countryman oblige me with some money?'

'Well,' said the fat man. 'So you are a Romanian. Where are you from?'

'Ploesti,' answered George, truthful for once.

'From Ploesti!' cried the other, and slapped his thighs in amusement. 'Good old Ploesti! Does it still stink so much of petroleum?'

George nodded seriously. 'I haven't been there for many months,' he answered, 'but when I left it it still stank to heaven.'

'You must tell me all about Ploesti,' said the fat man. 'I have not been there for a long time, so come to my office this afternoon and we will have a talk. You seem to be a bright and intelligent youngster. Here are five francs. Buy yourself something to eat. And here is my address.' He produced a visiting card:

M. ANATOLE CARCOLA
Directeur General
Carcola & Cie., S.A.
rue du Mont de Piété
Marseilles

Carcola & Compagnie, Société Anonyme was housed in a ramshackle building of two storeys which seemed almost ready to fall over into the rue Mont de Piété. The address was a standing joke with all Monsieur Carcola's acquaintances, for *mont de piété* means 'mountain of pity' or, in the colloquial language of the period, 'the pawnbroker'. Which, Carcola would explain, was quite coincidental. For Carcola & Cie. were one of the leading firms of ship-chandlers, and in their huge cave-like vaults a sailor could buy anything from a length of rope to a life-boat. For his Oriental clientele Carcola kept a special stock of erotica and supposed aphrodisiacs, as well as an up-to-date list of new recruits to the port's army of harlots.

During the long talk George had with Monsieur Carcola that afternoon he told him some of his adventures since leaving Constantinople. It was probably the wish to impress, though George maintained afterwards that it was the opportunity to talk freely in his native language, that loosened his tongue. Whatever the reason, George's 'Confession' amused Carcola, who had already formed a quite correct opinion of his young compatriot. Being a fair judge of character and knowing his Romanians, he did not believe for a second that George would ever be unnecessarily honest—it would be too much out of the national character.

'Why did you leave Romania?' he asked. 'You could have sailed out with the navy if you had waited.'

George remembered the water-logged training ship *Mircea*, and the few second-hand Russian clippers anchored off Galatz, and the slim-waisted, perfumed officers who preferred to sit in offices ashore, waiting for the delivery of French and German ships that never came, and shook his head. 'You do not know the Romanian Navy,' he answered. 'To have waited for them to sail away, I could have been an old man, with callouses on my hands—and on my behind— and crippled with rheumatism!'

'All right, you can work for me,' said Carcola, laughing. 'No hard work, to harden your hands,' he added, seeing George's rather unenthusiastic face. From a desk he took a large packet and gave it to George. 'Sell them aboard the boats from the Levant,' he said. 'The price is five francs each, and you can keep one franc of each sale. Here are one hundred cards.'

George opened the packet. It contained the dirtiest post-cards he had ever seen, even in not-so-squeamish Greece.

'You will do good business, my boy,' said Carcola reassuringly, when George hesitated. 'And you need not be afraid of the police. This is a free and broadminded country. Should you have trouble, just mention my name, the police patrols always buy their clothes here—at bargain prices. But be careful of priests and monks. They will skin you alive if they get you. They will hand you over to the moralists at the *préfecture* for having offended the Church. There not even I can help you. And what is worse, they will burn my cards as they have no regard for money.'

In a single week Manolesco sold several hundred cards to the sailors. One day Carcola, after having counted the money, called him back. 'Is that all you have?' he asked.

George did not understand. Did his countryman want to trap him by some trick? Carcola smiled. 'What I mean is, when you walked off the boats, did you just leave them like that? Or, maybe, did you find things . . . lying about?'

As George did not answer, Carcola said: 'Come, come, tell me, or are you such a fool as not to know what is good for you?''

To be called a fool by Carcola was not to George's liking. With a wry smile he confessed that there were a few things lying about, a watch in a cabin, a few foreign bank-notes, a leather brief-case, some shirts. 'I could not leave them . . .' he said. 'They might have got stolen. . . .'

'Quite so,' said Carcola. 'Let's see what you have got.' George showed him his acquisitions.

'In future,' said Carcola, 'do not bother to "find" shirts or leather cases. I will give you fifty francs for the watch and for the Austrian money. Although it is not worth it. I can always sell little things in my shop, but try to get me good stuff!'

At this moment began George's real business relationship and close friendship with ship-chandler and 'fence' Anatole Carcola.

'There are no crooks,' Carcola would say. 'Only honest men. Show *anyone* the way to make a bit of easy money and he will listen to you. If then you can put something over him he will not even notice that he has been cheated. As for me, George, I am absolutely honest!'

Before George left, Carcola gave him more advice: 'I think you will go a long way, but never be petty. The risk for a handkerchief is the same as for a diamond brooch. Bring me diamonds!'

'Diamonds do not just lie around waiting to be picked up,' protested George.

'That is just where you are wrong, my friend,' retorted Carcola. 'They do—if you choose the right company. As a matter of fact, here in Marseilles you are wasted. Here we have too much riff-raff and nobody trusts anybody in this harbour of thieves.'

George went straight out and bought himself a new suit, new shoes, hat and cane and put on one of the shirts he had 'found'. Then he hired a carriage to the New Town, and gave himself a first-class dinner with champagne. With nearly 300 francs still in his pocket he thought of joining a card game in the back room of a café in the Old Town, to see if he had retained his genius for cards. He had. But Marseilles was not Ploesti, nor Athens, nor Constantinople. It was a tough city, whose inhabitants resented being cleaned out at cards. On the way home to the small hotel where he had taken a room, he was attacked, beaten up and robbed of everything he possessed (including his new clothes) and dumped in his shirt and underpants in a filthy alley. He was lucky to stay alive. In the small hours of the morning, shivering, he stumbled through empty streets to the premises of Carcola & Cie. and there huddled in the doorway until the morning, dreading that a police patrol might pick him up.

Carcola did not laugh when he saw him, but clothed him and gave him money for breakfast.

'If you had told me that you are a card-sharper,' he said, 'I could have warned you not to demonstrate your art in the Old Port. Now, you would be better to leave town. There is a train tomorrow to Paris. You can work your way to the capital.'

George joined the 'Slaughterhouse Navy'. Every week about 1,000 sheep left the Harbour Station of Marseilles for Paris, destined for the slaughterhouse. With the train went ten guards, each one in charge of seventy-five to one hundred sheep.

During the four-day journey many of the ewes delivered lambs in the trucks. It was an unwritten law among the guards that these new-born lambs were their perquisite; they sold them *en route* to farmers standing beside the tracks and waiting for them. Acknowledging this fact, none of the guards received any payment from the transport company.

When the train arrived in Paris and the guards had driven the sheep to the nearby Abattoir La Vilette, George found himself with ninety francs. After a much-needed bath, he bought a second-hand suit, shoes and linen, threw away his old clothes, and boarded an express omnibus to the centre of the city. At last he had arrived in Paris, and he decided to celebrate this event with a champagne lunch on the café terrace of the Grand Hotel in the Place de l'Opéra.

Chapter 3

Jacques, the head waiter at the 'Bouillon Duval' in the rue Bac, shuffled through the rows of tables to George's chair, flicked his red napkin under his arm, and bowed slightly. 'Monsieur,' he said politely but with the merest touch of irony, 'has Monsieur made his choice?'

'Yes,' answered George. 'I'll have some *soupe à l'onion*, to be followed by lobster with *sauce tartare*. The rest I will order later.'

'Thank you, Monsieur,' answered Jacques. 'However, I am so sorry, we are out of lobster today.' He pointed to a huge gilt-framed mirror behind the desk of the plump woman-cashier, on which the dishes available had been crudely chalked. 'Also, there is no onion soup, Monsieur, it will not be ready before the late supper. All that is left is some fricassee of veal and perhaps a cheese afterwards. Would you like white or red wine?'

'All right, Jacques,' said George. 'So it is hash again as usual. I only wish I could have some oysters and champagne. Never mind. Bring the hash along.'

For the last few weeks George had been a regular guest at the 'Bouillon Duval'. Of his own accord he would never have dreamed of entering the unpretentious restaurant. Jacques the waiter was a neighbour in the house in the rue Vivienne where George had taken lodgings. Several times the good-natured waiter had helped George, who told him that he was a student, and was waiting for his monthly allowance. Jacques took him to 'Duval' and paid for his meals.

'I will repay you with interest,' promised George, 'the

very moment I am in the money. I will buy you a fantastic dinner with lobster and onion soup. I adore onion soup.'

The onion soup became a standing joke. When George surprised Jacques one day by paying his own bill at Duval, and even bought his friend a cognac, Jacques wondered but did not ask questions. But when he met George on the landing at their lodgings, dressed in a new suit, with yellow gloves, a huge silk cravat and patent leather shoes, he said: 'Hah, you have made a pile.' He opened the door of his room. 'Come in for a moment.'

'George,' he said after closing the door carefully, 'I thought you were a student at the Sorbonne?'

'And . . .?' said George.

'Well, you must be more careful. I saw you today at the *bon marché* in the rue Bac.'

'Why didn't you call me?'

'You were very occupied,' smiled Jacques, 'ahem . . . buying things. . . .'

'You mean, you saw me . . . ?'

'Oh yes, mon ami, you chose very carefully, and I wondered where you got the money. But I did *not* see you pay!'

'You did not? So what?'

Jacques shook his head. 'So . . . nothing. But one day you will have an unpleasant surprise.'

'If you mean they'll catch me,' said George unabashed, 'forget it. They have to get up very early to catch George Manolesco.'

Jacques shrugged. 'I hope you know what you are doing . . . but so did I some years ago. I got three years.'

'Very sad,' nodded George. 'But why should I? I am grateful to you for telling me of a professional blunder on my part; and you can rest assured that I will look after myself. I hope you will not yell the story all over the place; that would be very embarrassing.'

George decided to end his raiding expeditions in the department stores, to drop all 'minor operations', and try his hand with diamonds. Having made up his mind *what* to steal, it was now a question where. The obvious place was a jeweller's, and during his walks through Paris he had noticed that the biggest and wealthiest seemed to be Fontana, in the arcades of the Palais Royal. For several days he kept the shop under observation, and then, feeling that in his new clothes he could be taken for a rich young man-about-town, he entered the shop and asked the salesman to show him some jewellery, to study the routine of sales procedure.

For his first major robbery he chose the evening, when the smart people of Paris went shopping to avoid the common crowds. At 8 p.m. he drove in a hired carriage to the brilliantly-lit shop. The salesman who had shown him gems before recognized him and rushed to the entrance.

George put his top hat and cane on a small glass table and, caressing the beginnings of a moustache, asked to see some bracelets. 'After all,' he said to a flattered salesman, with the man-to-man confidence of the boulevardier, 'I think I owe Madame some kind of token of my appreciation.'

'Quite so,' answered the salesman and produced trays of jewellery. After a long conversation, Manolesco chose a small bangle from one of the first trays he had seen and instructed the salesman to have it sent to him at a fictitious address. It was now near closing time and the shop was emptying quickly. Suddenly as if the idea had just occurred to him, he turned round and asked: 'I am much interested in some unmounted diamonds. Have you got any?'

'I had the salesman rattled,' recalled George. 'To show me diamonds would take him quite a time and, wanting only to get home to his wife and supper, he would certainly try to rush the proceedings.'

For three weeks George had practised in his lodgings, switching stones from an imaginary tray for one held in his hand. When he saw among the diamonds shown, a few gems similar enough to the cut–glass 'diamond' he had bought for a few sous, he went into action. Now jewellers, naturally enough, always carefully watch the hands of their clients when jewellery lies about openly, and George had anticipated this. As he had calculated, the eyes of the salesman were fixed upon his *right* hand. George was ambidextrous; with his *left* hand he secured without difficulty two stones totalling about seven carats, made his selection from the tray and asked for it to be sent to the fictitious address.

This, his first major *coup*, brought him £1,400. The next morning he went to a fence behind the Place Clichy to sell the stones. But the prices offered were so low that he disposed only of the smaller one, for 1,000 francs, and posted the other one to Carcola in Marseilles, with a little note, reading:

'I hope this will please you. Five thousand francs in return would please me.'

Six days later he received a visitor who introduced himself as Signor Machinelle and said that he had been asked by their mutual friend Carcola to give George 3,000 francs. 'In future,' added Machinelle, 'if you have any watches to be repaired you can always come and see me. Here is my address.'

He chuckled at his own wit and left with twinkling eyes.

With the acquaintance of Signor Machinelle, George's establishment as an important thief was complete. He took comfortable rooms in the centre of the city and in the next few weeks followed up his success at Fontana's with repeat performances at several big jewellery stores, and then visits to Machinelle's little shop behind the Bastille. George himself estimated in later years that during the short time of his Paris activities he stole jewels and other things worth 600,000 francs. The *préfecture de police*, however, claim that he multiplied his claim by ten! It was still a comfortable amount of money, even allowing for the fact that George received from the 'fence' but part of the real value.

He could now live in the grand manner once more. He bought himself clothes for every occasion, hats, cravats, linen. He acquired a pony and trap to drive around town and hired a groom to look after it. He was accepted as a regular at L'Horloge, the café in the Champs-Elysées where the gay blades of the period met over an aperitif. He became the darling of all the head-waiters on Montmartre. He was always accompanied by a woman, but changed them so often that the idlers on the café terraces along the tree-lined streets lost count. Nobody asked who he was or where his money came from. In the world of Parisian men-about-town such questions were *rigolo*.

He had money; he was an interesting conversationalist, perhaps the best recommendation in a set in which one must never be bored. He was always seen at the right places, at vaudeville theatre first nights, at dances in the fashionable hotels, and at the luxurious *boîtes de nuit* around the Place Clichy. He was always dressed like a fashion plate and many of the variations of style that he introduced into his own dress were carefully observed and copied. He was on the way to becoming an arbiter of elegance for young lay-abouts. Once he discovered in a wood-turner's shop a little figurine of a nude woman and had it mounted as the handle of his ebony stick. In a very short time many of his café acquaintances carried sticks with similar handles. He never spoke of his own affairs, and his role as the lone wolf with an aura of mystery made him still more interesting.

Then one morning one of the more popular and sensational newspapers of the capital published a story that reminded George that he was still on very slippery ground. 'A thief has specialized in robbing the great jewel stores of Paris,' reported the paper. 'Nobody knows who he is, where he comes from. He is described by the jewellers as a charming, young and well-dressed man. He speaks French perfectly, although with a faint foreign accent. Six big jewellers have lost a fortune through his clever manipulations. Up to now these jewellers, whose names are household words in Paris, have preferred to bear their losses rather than endure the bad publicity; nor do they want the police blundering about their so-refined establishments and frightening off their wealthy customers. Now they have employed a number of private detectives to pose as salesmen in their shops and to keep a watchful eye on all customers.' With typical Parisian irony the reporter ended: 'They have closed the stable door after the horse has bolted. It is very doubtful that our friend with the talented long fingers will take up the challenge and have himself arrested.'

George read the report with a certain satisfaction; it was an acknowledgement of his omnipotence as a shop-lifter. Now it was time to change his tactics. His income had been large, but his spending ability matched it. That nobody suspected him, despite his sudden appearance as a young rich waster, did not surprise him. Paris was crowded with visitors from all over the earth who had come for the Great World Exhibition, soon to be opened, and to stare at the gigantic iron tower which the engineer Eiffel had built to dominate the whole city. The police were paying no attention to the Smart Set, most of them sons of wealthy bourgeois families. The jewellers' private detectives, according to the Press, insisted that the thefts had been carried out by an organized gang. The papers warned the public that with thousands of wealthy visitors, pickpockets swarmed through the city, most of them Englishmen sent over by a central organization and always returning with their loot to London, out of reach of the French police. Nothing was easier than to escape the police even if caught in the act, commented one writer. 'You simply hire a carriage and the poor *agent de police* will be unable to follow, for the thief-catchers of the *préfecture* do not allow their employees to spend money on carriages!'

George decided to give the jewellers a rest. His new victims were easily found—through the Press. *Figaro* nearly every day published a column of Parisian society news, announcing tea parties, dinners, garden parties and receptions. It was easy to gate-crash many of the functions if one was but well dressed and well spoken. Now, sporting a small moustache, very sure of himself, George would ride up to the great house he had selected, and send his groom home. He entered by the back door, and if he was stopped there by a footman or maid, would pretend to be slightly drunk and say: 'Had to have a breath of air . . . you know. And now . . . I want another cognac . . .' and push past the smiling servant.

He preferred garden parties where he merely had to jump over a low wall or squeeze through a hedge. He would go to the buffet and take a plate of delicacies and a drink and disappear into the crowd—often as many as 300. Then he would explore the upper part of the house.

'It is surprising,' he recalled, 'what a load of jewels ladies carry. Often they cannot wear them all and I always found plenty left in the dressing-rooms on the first floor.'

If he were stopped during his explorations he would explain that he did not feel well and was looking for a place to rest for a few minutes.

'At the garden party in the Palais of the Marquis de Massor,' he recounted, 'a sympathetic maid led me into a boudoir with a fortune in gems on the dressing-table. I did not touch a thing. I just made a mental note of the make and position of a small wall-safe, which the occupant had left open, as if in a hurry.'

George was very careful and very cunning nowadays. In most cases, after having studied the layout of the house and possible locations of safes and other places for jewellery, and taken perhaps a few small items—'just to cover my expenses' —he returned to the reception.

In the ballroom a dance would then have started, and from the young women appraising him, he chose a partner, not so much for her beauty as for the jewellery she wore. After a dance or two would come the suggestion of a little walk through the gardens or on the glassed-in terrace. A gallant compliment or two and if the first amorous advances were not repulsed—which was not often—a lingering kiss. And when the girl gently freed herself from the embrace, the necklace would be in George's pocket.

When Mademoiselle discovered the loss of her jewels, George was never suspected. He was the charming young man who was so desolate at the loss, so helpful in looking for the necklace, even suggesting that the police be called— something always rejected with horror by the victim, since this could not be done without involving her illustrious hosts in a public scandal. This fear of scandals and avoidance of the police made it much easier to sell the stolen goods, and George could use the regular market in second-hand jewellery, where the prices paid were ten times better than Machinelle's. Brazenly he went into a jeweller's shop to offer his 'family pearls'. There were so many gem shops and traders in Paris, all keen on a bargain, that he easily avoided using the same firm twice.

* * *

The Duchesse de Trevolle was a lucky woman. She was rich, beautiful, witty. For the last twenty-five years her love affairs had been the delight of Paris, widely discussed in the boudoirs, in the *salons*, in the fashionable clubs and in the cafés of the Bois de Boulogne and the Champs-Elysées. At fifty-five, she retained the figure of a girl of twenty, the vitality of a debutante, and an insatiable appetite for men. 'La Trevolle' always had her eye on men and preferred them young, handsome and virile. She made no secret of her nymphomania, but did try to conceal her real age. She nearly met her match at a reception at the Imperial Court of Napoleon III, more than twenty years earlier.

Empress Eugenie, who disliked the vivacious woman always surrounded by young Guards officers, said to her sweetly: 'I forgot to convey to you my best wishes on your twenty-fifth birthday last week, Duchess. Surprising how time goes by. I remember very distinctly your last twenty-fifth birthday . . . wasn't it five years ago?'

The Duchess curtsied and smiled. 'Almost correct, Your Imperial Majesty,' she replied. 'Only it was ten years ago that I had my first twenty-fifth birthday. Since then I have celebrated it every year and I hope I will be able to go on celebrating it for another decade, or even longer.'

The Trevolles, who belonged to one of the oldest French noble families, together with a few rich landowners, retained their titles by courtesy of the *République*. When Paris changed from a battlefield to the most glamorous city in the world, the Duchesse de Trevolle still shocked the city.

A newspaper columnist heard that her love for the male went so far that she now employed only muscular men-servants, for whom she herself designed tight-fitting livery that provokingly emphasized their masculinity. The newspaperman went to her Palais to find out if this were true, and asked her the impertinent question of her real age.

'That is not a very gallant inquiry,' she replied. 'But I will answer you. I never try to think of my age. I am as young as I feel. And you can believe me, I feel very young indeed.'

'You *are* young, Madame, and beautiful,' the newspaper-man said. 'That is the kernel of the question. Have you discovered the elixir of eternal youth? What is it? How do you do it?'

'It is quite simple, mon ami,' answered the Duchess with an angelic smile; 'I hate going to bed without a man.'

That retort was a bit too strong even for the tolerant Paris Press of that day, but it went the rounds until everyone in Paris had heard it.

The *bal masqué* at the Palais de Sagan was the great event of the season of 1889, and George decided to attend it, encouraged by enthusiastic advance articles in the Press. It was forecast that 800 guests would be present. They would consume 500 lobsters, 300 chickens, ten gallons of ice cream, and 2,500 bottles of wine and champagne, served by eighty footmen, among them twenty detectives lent to the Prince de Sagan by the *préfecture*. The newspapers afterwards said that the jewellery on display was worth £5,000,000.

George had no intention of robbing the guests of their precious stones under the very eyes of detectives. He would get considerable pleasure out of mingling with the Polinchelles, Dominoes, Chinese coolies, Columbines, Turkish harem women, Marie Antoinettes, Harlequins, knights in pasteboard armour, and hundreds of masked figures, each a bearer of one of the great names of France, such as the Chambruns, the Rothschilds, the Duc de Bellevue and the Vicomte Azevedo.

He was sauntering through the crowded ground-floor *salons* of the huge Palais when, near the cold buffet in the dance hall, he brushed against a woman disguised as a page boy, in gold-embroidered silk cut-away and velvet *culottes*, her slim legs in white silk stockings. Her brilliant golden hair sparkled under the hundreds of candles on the crystal chandeliers, contrasting with the deep red mask on her face. As George started to apologize, the woman, gazing steadily

at him through the eye-holes of her mask, and holding him
by the arm, said in an extraordinarily deep voice: 'Wait a
minute, young man.'

George, like a number of other men guests, did not wear
an elaborate costume but only a coloured cape slung around
the shoulders over his exquisitely cut tail coat which emphasized his wide shoulders and narrow hips. He wore a small
black mask.

'You look very good to me,' continued the woman after a
few seconds' appraisal. 'Let us discover whether you can
dance!'

Manolesco was not a bad dancer but his partner was
superb. After the first waltz they stopped. 'Not bad, my
friend,' she said. 'Let us sit out the next one.' It was George's
turn to be invited to the terrace!

She led him to a vast, dimly-lit conservatory. Half
hidden under the groups of palms placed everywhere,
couples were sitting close together, many tightly clasped in
each other's arms. George was puzzled. As they danced he
had inhaled the sense-stirring perfume she wore, had felt
her warm body move sinuously against his own, rippling
with a youth belied by her deep, mature voice. Now he slid an
arm round her waist to bring her close for a kiss and with
the other hand tried to remove the tantalizing mask. She
pushed his hand away. 'Not so fast, young man,' she said.
'Or are you afraid of buying a cat in the bag? The time for
unmasking has not been announced yet. But, if you must,
you may kiss me.'

George knew she mocked him and stepped back a pace to
bow stiffly, ridiculously under the circumstances. 'At your
service, Madame,' he said coldly.

She burst into a peal of laughter. 'Quite a gentleman!
You *are* a gentleman, aren't you?'

'Definitely, Madame,' answered George ironically, 'even
at a *bal masqué*.' He had found his composure again.

'I was just wondering,' said she. 'I have seen you a few
times lately at garden parties and receptions. Impossible to
mistake such a figure as yours, mon ami. But I could never
find anybody who knew you well enough to introduce us.

Have you no name? Who are you? You are not a friend of our charming host, the Prince, or are you? Are you a sneaker-in? A gate-crasher? Come . . . tell me.'

George was intrigued by this, his first challenge.

'Madame,' he retorted, 'is it not most unusual to ask a man to name himself at a *bal masqué*? Are not all of us anonymous, just masks?' Then, tearing off his own mask he continued: 'However, your wish is a command. My name is George. I have *not* been invited, but I came here because I wished to dance with you!'

'An excellent answer, chéri; you are not at a loss for an answer. One day you will create a sensation with that classical face and that figure. Are you a passing vision, or do you live in Paris?'

George, a born gambler, replied easily now. 'I do live in Paris, and should you wish to know what I do here, I could say I came to see the Exhibition. But that would not be true. I am a thief by profession, Madame, but you need not be afraid, I have taken this evening off! And . . . now that we have arrived at confessions, who are you, Madame?'

Without a word she began to remove her mask, coquettishly sliding it down from her face, first to disclose large blue eyes filled with an expression George could not fathom. He did not yet know who she was, much less that she was 'La Trevolle'. Now her eyes gleamed with the thrill of the huntress, the huntress so rarely denied her prey. When the mask came fully away George saw delicate, beautifully-etched features, a *petite* nose, mischievously curving lips, cheeks without wrinkles. She could be thirty.

Still she did not tell her name. 'I see you cannot place me,' she said. 'And that is something very new to me. Very interesting, very exciting! Nobody could say that you have fallen for my name . . . if you have fallen at all.'

George realized that by failing to recognize this lovely woman he had betrayed the fact that he simply did not belong in her society. But knowing that attack is the best defence, he took her head gently between his hands, drew her easily to him and kissed her. Her lips were sweetly warm, cordial but with an element of experienced restraint, and after a second or two she pushed him away.

'We have a public here, mon Georges,' she said. 'I do not like to get . . . er . . . tuned up before curious eyes. Let us go.' She put on her mask again and so did George. They left the conservatory arm in arm and in the entrance hall she called a footman for her wrap.

'I hope I do see you again, Madame,' said George rather disconcerted by her matter-of-fact behaviour. 'Would you permit me to escort you home?' He cursed himself for having sent away his own personal carriage.

'Thank you,' she said. 'But I have my own carriage waiting.' And then, mercifully, she added: 'Why do you not come with me for a cognac and a coffee . . . that is, if you really wish to?'

'It would be an eternal shame to forgo an hour in your presence, Madame,' said George as he stepped after her into the white silk-cushioned interior of her carriage.

During the drive across the city they did not speak much. George sat rather aloofly beside Madame, although she had put her hand on his—he was deep in thought.

The Duchess's house behind the Etoile was exactly as George had visualized it. They entered a small, cosy hall whose walls were covered with hand-woven brocade. Several small oil paintings hung on one wall and against two others stood long mirrors. A velvet curtain hid the entrance to a small room furnished with complete disregard of cost.

'Sit down, Monsieur,' said Madame. 'Excuse me for a few moments. There is cognac, and coffee will be ready when I return.'

Alone in the room, George looked around with appreciation. A good fire crackled in the fire-place to one side of which was a wide and long gold-and-white settee almost smothered in cushions. Beside a miniature ivory-adorned grand piano stood a large glass case of antiques and curios. The walls were lined with paintings of severe-looking military men. The floor was covered from wall to wall with Oriental carpets, and in front of the fire was a large pure-white bearskin, complete with head and lolling tongue.

George walked across to study the glass case, partly from curiosity, partly from professional interest. There were the usual gold and silver spoons, figurines, chains, an old gold watch. There were porcelain figures and a score of gold snuff-boxes, studded with diamonds, just as he remembered them in the collection of the Comte de Boulogne. While he was still working out the value of the gold articles, someone entered the room and he turned around.

A white-whiskered, elderly man, in a red smoking jacket, silk scarf round his neck and a small pillbox cap on his bald head, had come into the room. He limped slightly, supporting himself with a stick.

'Monsieur,' he said in a high-pitched, old man's voice, 'I am enchanted to meet you. I hope you had a pleasant evening.' He peered through pince-nez. 'Let me look at you . . . you are a charming young man; trust Helene, she always has good taste.' Bowing, he introduced himself. 'Allow me, I am the Duc de Trevolle.'

'I,' answered George, bowing in return and then shaking the hand of the old man, 'am George de Manolesco, at your service.'

'Did you say Manolesco?' asked the Duke thoughtfully.

'. . . *de* Manolesco,' replied George swiftly.

'Quite so,' nodded the Duke. 'I knew a Baron Felicien Manolesco. We met him several years ago at the Spanish Embassy. I believe he was a Russian nobleman.'

'Felicien!' said Manolesco eagerly. 'Fancy that! He comes from our Ukrainian line . . . I myself am a Romanian, Monsieur.'

'How fascinating,' twittered the old nobleman. 'Did you tell Helene? She will be thrilled. She was very fond of Felicien, and it made her very sad when he had to return to his country so suddenly.'

George was about to answer when Madame returned and saved him from devising too complicated a story. She had changed into a Japanese-style yellow silk kimono with a high neck and buttons down the front. But it still revealed fleeting glimpses of her legs as she sat on a low chair and started speaking disapprovingly.

'Robert! You should not be up so late.' And to Manolesco:
'I see you have met my husband.'

'Chéri,' said the Duke animatedly, 'did you know that
Monsieur is a relation of our friend Felicien?'

'Indeed?' said Madame drily and looked at George, who
stood a little tensely by the mantelpiece. 'How very charming. Please, do be seated, Monsieur.'

To her husband once more she began: 'Robert, you are
very careless——' But he interrupted her irritably: 'I know,
I know, but you are worrying too much about me. I am
going back to bed. Excuse me, Monsieur, I am not too
well. A left-over from the war; a bullet hole from the *salles
Boches* still hinders my movements. However, I do not wish
to bore you, I trust you will come again. Do you play
chess?'

'I do,' said Manolesco, 'but I am not a master.'

The Duke laughed, bowed and limped towards the door.
There he turned around. 'Do not consider me rude, Mon-
sieur, to leave you . . . and please, do not be too late, Helene.
Bonne nuit.'

The door clicked shut and Madame shot a fleeting con-
spiratorial smile at George. Saying nothing, she walked
slowly to the piano and George watched the light reflected
from the haunches that rippled beneath the yellow silk of
the kimono. Sitting down she ran her fingers slowly and softly
over the keys; then came a small, beseeching melody and the
room grew intimate. The entrance of a footman with a tray
of coffee and sandwiches broke the moment. He was a huge
young man, looking to George more like a circus ring-
master than anything else in his short grey jacket and blue,
tight-fitting trousers.

Without taking her eyes from the piano, the Duchess said:
'Thank you, Philippe. Turn down some of the lights, then you
may go to bed.'

For a few seconds the Duchess continued to run her
fingers idly over the keys; then she rose and walked swiftly
to George, sitting on a low stool by the fire. George could
read nothing on the face that gazed down at him. He hardly
dared make a move. He did not even know if he wanted to.

He was as shy as the night when the Comtesse de Boulogne had seduced him.

The Duchess stared steadily down at him, then turned to one side to pick up a silver plate of sandwiches. She placed one on his plate, looking unswervingly into his eyes as she did so. George dropped his own eyes and then held the gaze. He saw that the first two or three buttons of her kimono had been deliberately undone, revealing her milky throat and the blue-white flesh stretched tautly across her collar bones, infallible betrayer of a woman's age.

The cynic in George got the upper hand. 'Older than I thought,' he said to himself. 'But she *has* lovely legs. It is a consoling thing that women deteriorate from the head downwards . . . the legs are the last to go!' Feeling more sure of himself now, he stood up and, taking her arm, steered her to the settee and sat on her left.

In the heat of the room the scent of the woman beside him rose aphrodisiacally, demandingly almost, and for the briefest moment once more George felt frightened, a small boy laying siege to something that would rebuff and hurl him away in the next minute or two. Later he recalled that, to his own surprise, he remained calculating. He found himself examining his own motives and thoughts, about to take one of the most glamorous women of the age in his arms. She wore no jewellery that he could remove, even if it were safe to do so. This, then, was to be no quick profitable adventure; it needed time and skill. If it called also for some expenditure of his manhood and an investment of his charms in this elderly, experienced, blatantly passionate woman, it would not be unpleasant and might pay long-term dividends. Cautiously he laid his arm around the Duchess's shoulder and drew her towards him. She smiled encouragingly, but as close as this George could now see the faint etchings of time beneath her eyelids, the lines of experience on each side of the now wet and avid mouth. George's first kiss was tentative but she took control of the situation.

'Your coat hurts me, it presses on me here,' she said, touching her breast tenderly. Then she leaned forward to undo his coat.

'Stripped by a Countess in Turkey and now by a Duchess in Paris,' George thought. He protested. 'Madame,' nothing more intimate seemed to come easily yet. 'Madame, I am well able to take off my own coat.'

'I am sure you are, George, but it pleases me to do . . . this. . . .' With a swift motion she tore the cravat from his neck and threw it to the floor. George took her in his arms again. She grasped him even tighter, then sank her long, sharp nails into his back through the thin lawn shirt.

'You are so slow, George,' she whispered, and taking each of his hands in hers, she laid one on each breast, thrusting proudly towards him, so that his fingers rested on the parting of the kimono. Holding his wrists, she asked: 'Will you . . . or I?'

Challenged, half dreading what he would find, George ripped his hands apart, the kimono buttons scattered in all directions. He saw two perfect breasts, full and firm as they were the day the Duchess first celebrated her legendary twenty-fifth birthday. George gently kissed each breast in turn, then murmured: 'I want to kiss all of you.' Dropping down on his knees beside the settee he began slowly to undo the rest of the kimono. As the garment fell away, she sat up, facing him and panting slightly. She undid the buttons of his shirt and—unlike the Comtesse de Boulogne—she could have had no complaints for George's chest was now thickly covered with black hair.

Regarding him for a second, she smiled slowly, stood up suddenly, dramatically and gloriously naked. 'But,' she said, 'you have had all the fun. Strip, George, and do not be shy.'

When she spotted the scar on his thigh she touched it tenderly with a finger-tip and smiled up impishly at him. 'I see it does not impair your manly powers,' she said examining him closer. 'Ten centimetres to the right and you would be of no use to me, mon Georges!'

Instead of an answer he lifted her up and carried her towards the door.

'Oh, no, mon Georges!' she exclaimed, wriggling from his grasp and standing facing him on the bear rug in front of the fire. 'We do not have to be that conventional. Take me!

Take me here . . . and convince me that the bullet did you
no harm!'

George proved that his manhood was unimpaired, first
on the rug and then again in Madame's bed. Here, in a
brief interval—for she was all-demanding—the Duchess
said musingly: 'So, you are a Manolesco, and you are a
thief? What do you steal?'

He attempted to distract her by caressing her, but she
pushed his hand away and went on: 'You need not be afraid
that I might give you away. It would be a horrible waste to
have such a handsome young man as you put behind bars.
I do not care what you have done. But if you wish that we
should stay friends, then I do not want you to rob any more.
I have enough to handle in my own scandals. So let us forget
the past and think of the future!'

After that night George became a regular visitor to the
Palais Trevolle.

What surprised him most was not her nymphomania but
the fact that she made no attempt to hide her desires. Yet
nobody—even the Duke, 'my long-suffering husband'—
found anything extraordinary in this state of affairs. George
stopped stealing, as he had promised. But when his money ran
low he murmured from the Duchess's pillow that his situation was getting precarious. As he fully expected, next
morning one of her over-developed servants delivered to his
room a letter containing £400.

When as a matter of form he protested later in the day, she
replied simply: 'You are my man. I have plenty. Keep it, and
I keep you, chéri. And do not blush.'

George had by now discovered quite a lot about 'La
Trevolle', but felt only pride that he, George Manolesco,
had become the acknowledged lover of one of the richest
women in France, and certainly the most notorious. The
Duke was happy to see his wife happy—just as Helene had
said. As a matter of fact this young Romanian became one
of the few lovers of Helene he did not dislike. Duke Robert
was idolatrously fond of his wife and liked to see people
paying her homage. It was the Duke who facilitated George's
entry into High Society. Playing chess with a patient, if

bored George, and listening with amusement to the wonderful stories the young man told of his travels, the Duke offered to introduce him at his Club, the exclusive 'Cercle Agricole' for gentlemen farmers, who Madame mockingly described as *'les mastodonts'* and *'les pommes de terre'*.

Now George was invited to receptions and garden parties in his own right, always with Helene, as the accepted lover of the season. Having the ducal carriage at his disposal, he had sold his trap. If the bills for tailors, restaurants or losses at the Club became menacingly urgent, Helene was always willing to help. They were seen together at the new roller-skating rink in the Salle Wagram, at the performances of the water ballet in the huge swimming tank built at the Palais d'Hiver, at dances, and dining and lunching together. They were invited to meet the American inventor Edison to hear the demonstration of his phonograph to the Paris Press at the offices of *Le Figaro*, they drove in the Sunday morning circuit of the Bois de Boulogne, and were among the invited guests at the opening performance of Buffalo Bill's 'Giant Wild West Show', brought to Europe, complete with Indians and cowboys, wild horses and sharp-shooters, for the World Exhibition.

George became a member of several exclusive clubs in the rue Royale, and was rather careful with his card-tricks, ensuring that he was not a constant winner. Even so, to Helene's delight, he won a complete racing stable (although a small one) from a fellow member. For George there were no more meals at the Bouillon Duval on bare wooden tables. Now it was lunch at Durand's, at the Lion d'Or, at the sensational new Café Americain on the Boulevard des Capucines, and supper in the luxurious dining-rooms of the Grand Hotel or the Hôtel du Louvre near the Palais Royal, where one always met Helene's friends, the super-elegant Comtesse de Ludre, the Comtesse de Belbeuf, whose tea and garden parties were the most fashionable in Paris, and Vicomtesse de Brossia, the most amusing gossiper of them all.

But he did not forget his old friend Jacques, the waiter at Duval's. He took him to a gourmet's restaurant near the

Comédie française and treated him to a wonderful *souper*, lasting two hours. George always insisted that Jacques must have dreamed of this for the rest of his life.

But . . . small clouds were appearing on the love scene. During a reception he attended with the Duchess at the Palais d'Aremberg, Helene, without exactly creating a scene, accused him of making advances to one of her 'best friends', the Vicomtesse de B. George denied it and added that this was but an excuse to get rid of him. In mutual fury they drove back to the Palais Trevolle. There, as they arrived, waiting for the Duchess was one of the few men who had seen through George's camouflage at their first meeting, and had judged him for what he was. What was worse, he said so frankly and publicly. He was the young painter Toulouse-Lautrec, whom Madame had commissioned to paint her picture for George. George disliked him intensely, with the cruelty of a beautiful young animal for a brother not blessed by Creation with a straight body and even limbs. But Helene had a great affection for the brilliant cripple, valued his wit, and admired his art.

Toulouse-Lautrec was slightly drunk when they arrived, but he instinctively appraised the mood of the Duchess and said sarcastically: 'I see, you haven't kicked him out yet.'

George turned on his heel and left the house instantly. In his lodgings he wrote a note to Helene, saying that he would go away for a few days so that she could take time to consider their relationship.

It was an unfortunate moment for the affair to end, for George was short of money. It was now far too risky for him to steal. He was all too well known in the only worthwhile circles. But there were other gay and wealthy cities besides Paris; why should he not go away for a week or so and try his luck elsewhere? And then return with plenty of money and straighten out the trouble with the Duchess?

At once—he was a precipitate young man—he took a carriage to the station and was told that within the hour the Balkan Express would leave for Bucharest and Sofia, by way of Zürich, Vienna and Budapest. For 450 francs, the greater part of his remaining cash, he bought himself a first-class return ticket to Vienna and a sleeper, and boarded the train. He carried only a small but expensive calf hand case. When the train left the Gare du Nord at seven-thirty in the evening, he went to the dining-car and had a meal, returned to his compartment and slept, dreamless and undisturbed until the next morning, when the train had already passed the Swiss border. He arrived at Vienna's West Station at ten o'clock in the evening and took a *fiaker* to the *de luxe* Hotel Imperial on the Ring.

Vienna was gay and rich but not lucky for George. It reminded him too much of his native Romania, with swaggering officers in fancy-dress uniforms, coiffured and manicured, dragging clattering sabres behind them, seemingly with no worries in the world and nothing to do but to flirt with the women. The wine shops were packed with drinkers, the coffee houses crowded with newspaper readers, while beggars swarmed everywhere.

He did not like Vienna, not only because he spoke German badly, but he had no luck at cards in the second-rate clubs he visited, while Viennese jewellers were much more on the alert for crooks than in Paris. It was understandable! Vienna was so near the Balkans, and enough gentlemen with long fingers passed through daily to keep the police on their toes. When his money was finished in a few days he sold his case and left without paying the hotel bill. He sold his gold watch, gold chain and a small ruby ring and acquired a second-hand suitcase which he filled with stones wrapped in paper and moved over to the Grand Hotel. Here also, there was no opportunity to steal, so as soon as the bill was presented he fled, again without paying. This time he sold his first-class return half-ticket to Paris and booked into the Hotel Meisl & Schadn, older and less comfortable, but preferred by the landed gentry of the Danube Monarchy and some of the lesser nobility connected with the near-by Imperial Court. Here he committed one small robbery but was penniless after three days.

The Vienna police, however, relieved him of his worries when a Grand Hotel servant recognized him in the street. He was arrested and jailed while inquiries were made about him. They yielded little, only the unpaid hotel bills, and as the hotels held it beneath their dignity to charge George, the police issued an expulsion order for vagabondage, banning him from returning to Austria for ten years. He was put on a train to Switzerland—third class—and at the frontier station told to get out and walk across the border. Even so he was lucky. It had taken all his powers of persuasion to convince the Vienna police to let him go to Switzerland and not to Romania, which was where he should have been sent.

He rode on a market cart from the border to Rorschach on Lake Constance and from there he found his way to St. Gal. There he saw a poster announcing the opening of the Great World Exhibition in the Paris he should never have left. At the railway station in St. Gal he stole a handbag from a traveller for ticket money and arrived in Paris the day before the opening. He went first to Machinelle to borrow some money and then—with a gigantic bunch of roses—took a carriage to the Palais Trevolle in the rue de Iéna.

'Mon Georges!' cried Helene when he entered, but somehow the words had not the welcome of three weeks earlier. George knew he had gambled and lost. Helene had already bedded down his successor, and when George met him some days later at a fashionable restaurant, the two men got on very well.

For a time George continued his visits to the Palais Trevolle to play chess with the Duke, gambled in the clubs and sold his racing stable—on which he had never set eyes. Once he took Helene to the new restaurant, Tourtel, under the Eiffel Tower on the shore of an artificial lake. In this gourmet's paradise no prices were stated on the menu and the *maître d'hôtel* estimated the costs of a *dîner* or *souper* and whispered the amount due to the illustrious patron, who just paid up. But as soon as the meal was over, Helene rushed away to meet her new lover.

'She was so beautiful, so young in her new lace-covered tea-gown,' recollected George, 'that I was sorry I had lost her—and not only because of the money. She had now become really desirable to me.'

George thoroughly enjoyed himself when Helene asked him to escort her to a Romanian function at the Exhibition. It gave him deep satisfaction when he was introduced by the official host, Prince George de Bibesco, to shake hands with gentlemen he spent most of his time avoiding under normal circumstances—Monsieur Poubelle, Chief of the Paris police, Monsieur Barbier, President of the Court of Justice, Monsieur Barnaston, the Public Prosecutor of the *République*. Fingering in his pocket the gold from a theft that morning, George wondered what would happen if they knew who he really was!

A few months later, when leaving a jeweller's shop in the rue St. Augustin, George was arrested by the officers of his former fellow guest, Monsieur Poubelle, and held in the cells of the Correctionel de la Seine; and on June 11, 1890, Monsieur Barnaston demanded a sentence of four years hard labour. With a clever defence lawyer and some help from the Trevolle family, he received two years in the Prison de Gaillon. Very little publicity was given to George in the Press. The thief who had hoodwinked Paris for over a year received only small paragraphs in one or two papers. Then, there were more important things happening. In Germany a young and arrogant Kaiser had sacked his faithful servant Bismarck and rattled his sabre at the arch-enemy, France. Madame Sarah Bernhardt's sensational performances as *La Dame aux Camelias* enchanted the nation, and a young Australian, Madame Melba, was singing Gilda in *Rigoletto*. The Eiffel Tower had become the acknowledged symbol of the capital of the world, Paris, and England's Prince of Wales was a regular visitor to the city's uninhibited night life.

George now had to work for ten hours a day in a gang repairing the old prison. Once he protested against the brutalities of the guards, and for answer was transferred to the Prison de Maza, near the Gare de Lyon, on solitary confinement in a damp, windowless cell, and a diet of bread and water. When George was released in 1892, he had made several friends in the underworld of Paris, and was determined never to get caught again.

With only a few francs in his pocket, the result of two years' slavery, he was advised to go to his Consulate for help and, rather doubtfully, did so the next morning. But as soon as he had given his name and proved it with the ticket of release from the prison, he was shown with great civility into the private office of the Consul.

'Here I was, in clothes which I had outgrown,' George remembered later, 'yet a handsome, beautifully-dressed diplomat treated me with a courtesy so different from the usual behaviour of Romanian gentlemen.'

'Monsieur Manolesco,' said the Consul, 'we have been looking for you for the last ten months.' And seeing the uncomprehending face of his visitor, the Consul explained that George's mother, when she died, had left a substantial sum of money to be paid to him on his twenty-first birthday. 'As we could not find you, your father has been appointed trustee for the money and we will now contact Bucharest to arrange payment to you of your inheritance.'

Supplied with some money in advance, George left the Consulate and took a small room on Montparnasse. He lived quietly and modestly without even thinking of resuming his former occupation. Once or twice he visited Machinelle who knew about George's 'professional accident', but they were purely social calls. Then, after weeks, came a request to visit the Consulate again.

George was informed that his mother had left him originally 15,000 francs; but during his father's 'trusteeship' this sum had reduced itself to 6,000 francs, which the Consulate was instructed to pay over at once.

'How could they give money to the old crook?' cried George, 'he has lost it all at the card tables! If only he never had seen a playing-card!'

At first George thought of staying in Paris, but when a few days later he met the Comtesse de Biencourt in her own little trap and was cut dead by her, he decided it best not to stay in a city where he was far too notorious.

'I want to make a fresh start,' he told the Romanian Consul, who wholeheartedly agreed.

At the end of 1892 George embarked on the French 7,000-ton steamer *La Bourgogne* at Le Havre, as a first-class passenger for Canada.

Chapter 4

The storm began, as all good storms do, just as the stewards served the soup. In a few moments there was not a passenger in the dining-room except George Manolesco, who was not in the least affected and made a thoroughly good Sunday lunch before strolling through the empty public rooms to the smoking-room. Another passenger was sitting in a corner with a pack of playing-cards in front of him on the table. When George approached, the man looked up in surprise. He was a small individual with a long pale face and a pointed black beard, in a black broadcloth-coat and a gleaming top hat.

'Are you feeling well?' he asked doubtfully.

'Perfect,' answered George smiling. 'I have never felt better in my life.'

'I am glad to hear it,' said the little man. 'I was afraid that everybody had already gone back to bed to endure their agonies in private. It is getting rather boring. He moved a card from one pile to another. 'Do you play solitaire?' he asked. George shook his head.

'It is a stupid game,' added the man. 'Do you play poker?' George said he did.

'Excellent,' said the man; 'what are we waiting for?' He stood up to his full five feet, clicked his heels, bowed slightly and announced with great dignity: 'My name is Juan José Alfonso Cirrucio, Marchése de Passano. What is yours?' George also bowed, clicked his heels, and told him. Then he took a chair opposite.

'The best of luck to both of us,' said the Marchése, shuffling the cards. 'I hope you do not cheat?!'

74

'Monsieur,' answered Manolesco with an icy edge to his voice, 'that is an insult,' and as the other spread his arms in a Latin gesture of apology, he added: 'I assure you that I never cheat on a Sunday.'

They played all afternoon and through the night until dawn, when the storm also ended. George did not for once try any of his tricks, they were not necessary. The little Marchése lost from the beginning and at breakfast-time George was $4,000 richer.

'Not your lucky evening,' remarked Manolesco as they parted.

The Marchése smiled happily. 'Do not say that,' he answered. 'Unlucky at cards, lucky in love. Have you ever been in love?'

'I found love very complicated,' answered George.

'You might be right,' considered the Marchése; 'one could call it complicated, but it is *sweet! beautiful! wonderful!* Women . . . the only thing worth living for. Does your heart beat faster if you think of playing cards? No, it does not. What thrill can a game of cards give you? Money . . . bah, much too simple.'

Manolesco shrugged. 'I love the simple things in life,' he retorted, 'such as money.'

In a second session in the afternoon, George added another $1,500 to his capital which the Marchése paid with visible pleasure in anticipation of what it might add to his luck in love.

When they disembarked at Halifax, George had made up his mind. He had left France with the firm intention of staying honest, apart perhaps from a little cheating at cards on week-days, which he considered no crime. But the temptation to rob the Marchése was too great. The man was criminally careless with his money, his wallet was stuffed with bank-notes, and the obliging cabin steward had given George the information that he was one of the richest landowners in Spain. A few thousand dollars more or less would not affect him.

That evening, while the Marchése was looking through the windows of the dining-room of the Hotel Victoria at the girls passing by, waiting for George to join him, the latter went into the Spaniard's room but found nothing to take away, except a bundle of papers which he stuffed into his pocket, on the principle that one never knew what might be useful. The Marchése, a seasoned traveller, had deposited everything with the management.

Next morning George strolled through Halifax but did not like it at all. He decided to visit the World Exhibition in Chicago, said to be the wickedest city in the world. That, he thought, might be quite an interesting experience.

From the Chicago depot of the Erie Railroad, he took a cab to the newly-opened Hotel Vermont at Cottage Avenue, opposite Washington Park, a gigantic building seven storeys high, and booked a suite with a private bathroom on the sixth floor, his windows overlooking Lake Michigan. He was very impressed by Chicago with its fine shops, the electric signs, the cable cars, the elevated railways, the tremendous crowds in the streets. The hotel exceeded everything, however. It had 300 rooms and suites, electric light and gas in every room, it had two lifts, and a roof restaurant with the best view in Chicago. On its ground floor was a lounge the size of a railway station. The reception desk was as long as the Pont Neuf in Paris, and adjoining were half a dozen coffee rooms, buffets, breakfast rooms and bars. Well-dressed men and women swarmed in the main hall, the women wearing some tantalizing jewellery. In his twenty-dollar-a-day suite he experienced for the first time the blessings of central heating and running hot water. He liked Chicago, and the hotel seemed to him ideal for a thief.

As soon as he had tipped the boy who brought up his luggage, he started to explore the hotel to get his bearings. He walked up and down the corridors and tried one or two doors, but all were locked. In his room he discovered that they locked automatically, and silently cursed the efficiency of the Americans, who seemingly thought of everything, even of thieves. It was going to make things a bit difficult. When he returned to the entrance lobby he got a second shock, which gave him still more reason to curse American efficiency.

Leaving the lift, he was accosted by a stout man wearing a bowler hat. From under a long waxed moustache a large cigar jutted out. Around a pot belly hung a leather belt weighed down by cartridges and a huge pistol in a holster.

'Mister,' said the man, 'are you looking for something?'

George stopped and looked at him, hardly understanding the accent. 'Are you residing at the hotel?' asked the man. 'Have you gotten a room?'

George did still not know what the other wanted, and to get rid of him, shook his head.

'Waal,' said the man. 'You better come with me.' He took George's arm firmly and led him to a small office near the reception desk.

That was George's first encounter with a hotel detective, something he had never heard of until then. The situation was soon cleared up when the detective learned that George had not only a room but a suite in the hotel. George exerted all his charm as he told the detective and another one who had joined them, as best as his English permitted, that he was so impressed by the gigantic hotel that he had to see every corner of it. He received a friendly warning not to do it again in case he met a house detective who shot first and asked questions later.

'We don't like shooting our guests,' the detective added with humour. 'Only if they do not pay their bills.'

Full of mock indignation, George complained of his experience to Mr. Keller, a Madison Street banker recommended by the hotel, with whom George wished to open a bank account. Mr. Keller was more than sympathetic—it did not happen every day that someone walked into his bank with something like $12,000 to deposit. He telephoned the Hotel Vermont and personally vouched for Monsieur Manolesco, a valuable client of his bank, adding that he hoped they would in future restrain from Wild West manners and conduct towards distinguished foreign visitors.

To make amends he invited George to supper at Eugene Prager's famous European restaurant, which boasted of dishes 'cooked like Mother did in the Old Country'. Both Keller and Prager were of Bavarian stock, second-generation

Americans. Keller ordered a *Kalbshaxe mit Knödel* (calf's leg with dumplings), as typically Bavarian as the genuine Munich beer they drank from large *steins*. During supper George mentioned casually that he was expecting large sums of money at a later date, to which the banker responded eagerly and suggested that George should invest the money in shares, especially mining stock, which had a great future.

'It always interests me to make money,' said George. 'I would like, however, to leave this question until my cash arrives'—which made an excellent impression upon Keller. With painstaking Teutonic curiosity, Keller continued questioning; he wanted to know all about the wealthy George; here were rich pickings. This was, of course, the impression George wanted to create. George began to spin his tale, playing up to the German's latent love of the romantic and his awe of the aristocracy. They had already reached the sixth jug of beer and the atmosphere was convivial, ripe for confidence.

'Mr. Keller,' said Manolesco seriously, 'I cannot answer all your questions at the present for important private reasons, but as my banker you are entitled to know more about me. You must promise me, as a man of honour, not to breathe a word of what I tell you to anyone until I say so.'

Keller promised and shook George's hand.

'Well,' said George. 'First, let me tell you my real name. It is not Manolesco, which is only my incognito. I am the Duke of Otranto.'

Keller swallowed hard. 'Say that again, mister,' he stuttered. 'The Duke of . . . what?'

'Otranto,' repeated George a little haughtily. 'A most ancient English family—they fought in the Crusades! I have just won in the London Law Courts a suit which restores me to my rightful titles and fortunes.' He then continued with a fantastic story that claimants to the title living in England would not hesitate to kill him.

This sort of thing Keller could understand, having been born in Chicago and having grown up there. 'Did you come here to be out of danger?' he asked.

'Oh no,' said George. 'The family owns land in Canada

and in the State of Virginia. The moment I receive the necessary documents from London I will take possession of my houses and land, and appoint someone in America to look after them.'

A slight doubt still remained in Keller's mind. Why, if he was a member of the British aristocracy, did he speak such broken English? George explained that he had been brought up in France and very rarely visited his mother country. 'After the death of my parents it was too dangerous for me to live in one of our castles in the Midlands.'

George then suggested that after everything was settled Mr. Keller might be interested in taking care of his affairs. The banker was *very* interested and called for another jug of beer. When they parted, George took a carriage to his hotel, and Keller the elevated railway to his home in a lake-side suburb. During the half-hour journey he rather muzzily tried to figure out his commission as business agent for the Duke of Otranto.

The bankers, brokers and sundry share-pushers of the Chicago Stock Exchange were the first to know (under many oaths of strict secrecy) that a customer of Mr. Keller's banking house was a duke. Naturally they told their wives, just as George had planned. Everybody wanted to meet the Duke who was travelling incognito, and George was invited to teas, dinners and suppers. The hard working, shrewd businessmen of the 'Windy City' liked the young man who was always perfectly turned out, whose impeccable manners could only be called lordly. He reminded them of their parent's stories of the German and Austrian aristocrats. Clothing manufacturers, beer-barons, meat packers, corn traders held up the modest young man as a shining example to all their sons and daughters. His appalling English, with its smattering of French indiscriminately intermingled, was imitated by the younger men and women of Chicago, particularly the women, for *he* never chewed unlit cigars, never talked to them with a butt-end in a revolving mouth. He did not spit, not even into the omnipresent copper spittoons. When *he* talked to a lady he always stood up, and he kissed the hand of his hostess. On Sunday mornings he was seen going to church. He was an excellent dancer, in great demand at house parties, and when he demonstrated his incredible card-tricks, even the most boring party became a roaring success.

When he had no dinner or party engagement, George prospected the other side of Chicago. He called at most of the bars, restaurants and burlesque theatres on the wrong side of Chicago Avenue. His lusty appetite made him notorious even in the red light entertainment district which, with the arrival of thousands of visitors for the Columbia Exhibition, had grown to tremendous dimensions. He showered money right and left, on porters, chambermaids, waiters, doormen and buggy drivers. Now and then he took part in a poker game in one of the dozens of gambling halls, and mostly he won dishonestly. He avoided games with professional gamblers who had flocked to the Exhibition from all over the United States, preferring sensation-seeking businessmen and farmers from the Mid-West whom he met at his hotel. Now and then he went to the races, but as he always lost he gave that up.

A Grand Parade had been staged by the Exhibition organizers for Independence Day, July 4. George considered this day as most suitable to return some of the great hospitality he had received and invited eighty of his friends to a party in the Exhibition grounds. He hired two four-in-hand mailcoaches and took his party to the Midway Plaisance, where the German Hagenbeck Circus performed. Afterwards they went to the Exhibition restaurant for a long meal with beer and European delicacies, and in the evening he announced that he had hired the new propeller-driven ship *Chicora* for an all-night trip on Lake Michigan and breakfast at St. Joseph's.

It was a success in the Manolesco style. It ended with four engagements among the younger set, twenty speeches from his guests, hoping that the 'Dook' would remain in Chicago for a long time, and a bill amounting to $6,000, which lowered his assets to $2,000. But it was not really so expensive; for when George returned to his hotel after parting with his friends at the landing stage, he carried in his pocket a nice collection of brooches, pins, bracelets and gold watches, which he had found lying about in the *Chicora*'s cloak-rooms.

From an advertisement in the *Saturday Chicago Tribune*, he learned that:

PRIVATE PARTY
will loan on good security
or
BUY
diamonds, notes, receipts,
mortgages, insurances, or
any other valuables

George called at the address in First Dearborn Street and disposed of his loot without any questions being asked. Even the price was fairly good, for with the rush of visitors and money to Chicago, there was practically nothing which could not be sold in the city and for which there was not a demand.

* * *

At the end of six months in Chicago, and with a win at chemin-de-fer in the room of an hotel acquaintance, he had recovered $12,500 of the $20,000 he had spent in the United States. He could not now quite make up his mind if it would be wiser to leave the city immediately where, after all, the pickings had only been moderate, or to try one big *coup* and then disappear. Two events made him decide to leave as quickly as possible. The first was a friendly reminder from his friend Keller that his account was empty and a rather bold question about the long awaited money from England. Keller was clearly not impressed, this time, by George's evasions.

The second event had begun about three weeks earlier. At a meat packer's party in a brownstone mansion just off Astor Street and near the lake shore, George had met Margaret, the daughter of a Milwaukee beer baron. She was thirty-five, plain and plump and with mouse-grey hair. With all this she had to be a determined girl. The moment she saw the 'Dook' the cat-grey eyes lit up and she could not be moved from George's side. It was clear to everyone, including George, that she was intent on marrying him.

He was invited to Milwaukee to visit her jovial father, who was devoted to his unattractive daughter. George was shown the brewery and the palatial mansion, and was as impressed as he was expected to be. Father indicated bluntly enough that all would come to his daughter's husband. George fled and shunned a second visit to Milwaukee—but Margaret was not easily deterred. She wrote to him: 'Imagine, we could produce beer in bottles with a label featuring your portrait and calling it "Ducal Beer", from the Ducal Breweries of Otranto.'

George could imagine it and shuddered. He had occasionally considered marriage to a rich girl, but always dropped the idea. Margaret's plan was doubly ridiculous, not only because it would immediately lead to the discovery that there was *no* Duke of Otranto, but also . . . beer!

Keller, worried about his client's dwindling funds, advised him. 'The girl has millions, and her father told me she is stuck on you. He will give you a great job in his brewery and a salary of $100,000 a year. Grasp the chance—now!'

'It is very impressive,' condescended George, 'but such a marriage would endanger my English title and fortune.'

'Never mind,' said Keller, 'the old man has enough for both of you. And the title, well, I think she would get over the loss of that . . . she is really love-sick!'

George was adamant. 'I am not for sale,' he said proudly. 'A Duke of Otranto cannot be bought. Besides, I do not like the girl—and I do not like beer. I prefer champagne! I am going away from Chicago!'

He drove to his hotel and checked out, deciding to travel to New York. But when the carriage passed the railway depot in Van Buren Street, he stopped the coachman. In front of the Rock Island Railroad stood a huge wooden signboard, on which an oversized young couple were painted, walking happily hand in hand in a beautiful landscape; on the left were soaring mountains with snow-capped peaks; to the right, blue sea glittered in the sun. In the background was

a house with a porch and in front of it a buggy with two
children. The signboard proclaimed in huge letters:

GO WEST YOUNG MAN,
CALIFORNIA—THE LAND OF OPPORTUNITIES!

George, too, was romantic. He stared for seconds at the
picture of the enticing land, until the coachman gruffly
reminded him that he would miss his train to New York.
'Nix New York,' he said on the spur of the moment and
ordered the man to turn round and take him to the Union
Pacific station. When the evening Pullman train steamed
out of Chicago, George was firmly installed in a very
comfortable compartment for his three-and-a-half-day journey
to the Golden West.

*   *   *

For various reasons, George was not very popular aboard
the train, in marked contrast to his usual experience. The
ladies in the drawing-room car anticipated delightful hours
with the handsome young man and could not forgive him
for spending most of his time with a middle-aged woman in
the compartment next to him. The gentlemen in the parlour-
car resented his consistent luck at poker, which added a
clear $7,500 to George's capital in one long session on the
first day. The indignation of his fellow travellers did not
worry George who, satisfied with his haul, dedicated all his
time to the lady, whom he found extremely interesting from
several aspects. Most intriguing was the string of pearls
she wore in the dining-car each evening. On the last morning
of the journey George raided the crocodile-skin handbag left
for a moment on the seat of the compartment and put the
pearls in his pocket. On her return from a brief chat with a
casual acquaintance, the lady discovered her loss and raised
the alarm. By now George was sitting in the small barber
shop off the parlour-car, having his moustache trimmed. All
the compartments were searched but nothing was found. The
express had reached Stockton on the last stage of its journey
and more policemen, led by a sheriff, arrived to question

each passenger. The dusty, sweating sheriff, a huge silver star on his breast, approached George, who lounged smiling in the parlor-car.

'You have the compartment next to the lady,' began the sheriff.

'Certainly I am her neighbour,' said George. 'I have to be somebody's neighbour on a train. Which does not mean that I know anything about the pearls.'

'Aren't you mighty sure?' asked the sheriff, who had taken an instant dislike to the perfumed dandy.

George rose slowly from his chair and planted himself in front of the representative of the law. 'Sir,' he snapped, 'this is intolerable! Are you accusing me of being concerned with the disappearance of the lady's pearls? I ask you to watch your words. You apparently do not know to whom you are talking.'

A wide grin lit the weather-beaten face of the sheriff. 'Precisely,' he nodded. 'You tell me, mister. Who are you? And where are the pearls?'

Maliciously smiling passengers watched George's predicament. He stayed cool, arrogant and brazen.

'All right,' he said to the sheriff; 'come along with me,' and led him to his compartment. He took a small leather case from the rack and produced a piece of paper. The sheriff studied it with great concentration. It was plastered with red and blue seals and a number of signatures and stated that the bearer, the Marchése de Passano, was representing H.M. the King of Spain, and in three languages, asked all authorities to facilitate his duties.

'Well, I am sure sorry,' said the sheriff, returning the document to George. 'I don't aim to start a Spanish-American war.'

The passengers were allowed to return to their seats and the train proceeded on its journey. George walked down the corridor and retrieved the pearls from the place where he had hidden them in the guard's compartment at the end of the parlor-car. A few hours later the train arrived at Oakland Mole and the passengers transferred to the ferry boat for the twenty-minutes sea crossing of the bay to San Francisco.

George, taking leave of his desolated lady, offered his services should she need them in the strange city. Smiling through tears she accepted an invitation to dinner on a night to be arranged.

George drove from the waterfront to the Hotel California on Bush Street, a storey higher than Chicago's 'Vermont' and connected by a bridge to the Palace Hotel, opposite. He registered as the Marchése de Passano, enjoyed the elevator ride to his suite on the seventh floor, took a bath and changed his clothes. Lazing on a chair by the bay window, he felt that things had gone very well—thanks to the bundle of papers he had stolen in Halifax. He hoped that some love affair would console the real Marchése for the loss of the documents. He took the string of pearls from his pocket and let them slide slowly through his fingers, studying them lovingly. He did not yet know what to do with them, but devoutly hoped for a good price as consolation for all the trouble they had caused. Just then came a knock. Putting the pearls away again, George opened the door. Two men stood in the corridor—one George recognized as a passenger he had seen several times on the train. The other was a stranger. He was a fat man with a brown beard, wearing a grimy dark-grey suit and a matching high bowler hat. Over his red waistcoat was a leather belt with a pistol dangling at each thigh. The former train passenger politely raised his hat, but red-waistcoat pushed George aside and rushed into the room. He looked around and sat down heavily on a couch, putting his rather dirty shoes up on a table. Taking a long, thin cigar from his jacket pocket, biting off the end and spitting that out on the carpet, he lit up and spoke for the first time.

'Come on in!' he called to the other man who still stood at the door facing George. 'Sit down and make yourself comfortable.'

Furious, George threw the door wide open, looked from one intruder to the other and said with a choked voice: 'OUT!'

The man on the couch grinned and pushed his hat back to a more comfortable angle. He opened his jacket to disclose a badge on the red waistcoat. 'Police!' he said. 'Close the door, buddy, or do you want the entire hotel to listen to what I have to say?'

George gave the door a vicious kick to slam it shut.

'Now, now,' smiled the policeman. 'Take it easy, mister. Sit down and relax. I suppose you know Mr. Krull?'

Mr. Krull had been suspicious of George all the way from Chicago. Nobody could have so much luck at cards as George. He had watched his flirting with the woman whose pearls were missing and he was convinced that only George could have stolen them. He had gone directly to the police in San Francisco and told them so. Now the Captain of Detectives wished to have a word with the Marchése de Passano, at Police Headquarters, City Hall.

George listened in silence to the detective's explanation. Hand in pocket, he fingered the pearls. Only bluff could get him out of this situation.

Contemptuously he stared at the lounging detective and at Krull, still hat-in-hand by the door, and said in his most superior manner: 'I have never in my life experienced such an insult! Do you realize that you are accusing not only me, Juan José Alfonso Cirrucio, Marchése de Passano, but also the entire Kingdom of Spain, and her beloved ruler, the great King Alfonso, by suggesting that I am a thief? Just because I happen to be present when a necklace disappears?' Pointing an accusing finger at Krull, he continued: 'This man was present as well. Who says *he* is not the thief? I could accuse him as easily as he accuses me.' He paced angrily up and down the room for a moment and then stopped in front of the detective, for it had occurred to him that no harm could be done by securing the goodwill of this character.

'You,' he said, 'are but doing your duty and believe me I do not bear any grudge against you. I will gladly follow your advice and have a talk with your Captain of Detectives to clear up this matter once and for all. I will ask him to look into this man over here—you can see guilt written all over his face. We will soon discover the mysterious role he is playing in this not very pleasant affair.'

It sounded impressive.

'All right,' said the detective after a few moments. 'You

have had your say.' He rose, threw the cigar-end into a spittoon and grinned at Manolesco. 'You talk it over with the Captain,' he said. 'I'll be seeing you,' and took the arm of the white-faced Krull, led him to the door and out into the corridor. Before he closed the door, he turned around, flapped a half-raised hand, and said: 'Don't leave town, buddy, before you have your little chat. The chief is in his office at eleven tomorrow morning.'

When the door closed, George fell into a chair, exhausted. It took him a good half-hour to recover his poise. He found a hiding-place for the pearls under the window-sill, took his hat and stick, and left the hotel for a walk.

The first thing was to get rid of the pearls. Not a simple affair in a strange city if one was in a hurry and with the knowledge that the police were already suspicious. Walking along busy Market Street, a big jewellers in a block next to the Emporium Department Store attracted his attention. He entered the huge pillared sales-room and asked to see the manager. He was led past showcases full of gems up a marble staircase to the first floor, where he was received by an elderly, faultlessly-dressed man. George introduced himself as the Marchése de Passano and, in his mixture of French and English, told the manager that he required some information. A string of pearls had been stolen the day before from his wife. How might one recover it?

'I do not wish to go to the police,' he added. 'I hate publicity, as you will understand, being a diplomat on an important mission. Besides . . . my confidence in the police is not too great.'

The manager was not in the least surprised by George's request, but flattered and delighted to show off his French. He suggested that the Marchése should employ the services of a private detective.

George shrugged. 'I am a total stranger in your city,' he answered. 'Could you recommend one to me?'

'Yes,' answered the manager. 'If I say "private detective", however, I am being ultra-polite. The man I am thinking of is in constant touch with our numerous criminal element and specializes in just the kind of case as yours, the recovery of stolen goods. Insurance companies work with him; we, too, have employed his service on occasions—as the leading jewellers in San Francisco we, also, do not like publicity.'

George thanked the jeweller profoundly, after receiving the address. 'Now,' said the manager, as he shook George's hand at the door, 'be careful. He lives in a bad part of San Francisco, and I am certain that retrieving lost jewellery is not all the business he does. If you have too much money on your person I would leave it at your hotel.'

This was exactly the information George was looking for. He returned to the hotel, deposited most of his money in the manager's safe, and with only two ten-dollar pieces and the pearls in his pocket, sauntered off towards the Barbary Coast and Mr. Williams's office, five blocks away. Ten minutes walk brought him to a shaky wooden fence with a crudely-painted red arrow pointing to the door of a semi-derelict bungalow. The windows were covered with iron shutters and the house looked uninhabited. A sign at the door in half-vanished letters announced:

P. S. I. WILLIAMS
AGENT AND PRIVATE DETECTIVE

KEEP OUT
SHOOTING IN PROGRESS

Dusk was falling. George was ascending the wooden steps to knock at the door, when two shots sounded inside. Perhaps three seconds later, like an afterthought, came a third shot, much nearer the door. The door swung open, a man came out, saw George standing on the step and shouted over his shoulder to someone in the dark interior: 'Company, Pete! . . . Stop the artillery!' and walked off grinning.

The answer was another shot from the far end of the room. Then after a moment a kerosene lamp was lit and a man, naked to the waist, with a pair of tight-fitting leather trousers, and with a wide-brimmed cowboy hat on his head, pistol in one hand, lamp in the other, came to the door. He was the thinnest and tallest man George had ever seen, with a face looking like the head of a skeleton.

'Rats!' he announced in a deep voice. 'Rats! Hundreds of them. Have to shoot them, twenty a day at least. Otherwise they'd nibble the entire place away. You want to see me? Come on in, man, come on in. What can I do for you?'

The unusual appearance of Mr. Williams did not prevent George from taking an instant liking to the man; he had a strong feeling that he was the right person for the job in mind.

Carefully he put his question: 'Would you know how to dispose of a string of pearls, and where to find them if they had been stolen?'

Williams did not answer. He slowly raised his pistol and fired a shot into the semi-darkness of the bare room. 'Got him!' he exclaimed. 'A real fat one, too. That makes it two dozen today. Not bad, not bad at all. You bring me luck, young man. Now then, what was that about a string of pearls?'

George repeated, slowly: 'If one wants to get rid of a string of pearls, or to find a stolen one——'

Williams interrupted him. 'Make up your mind. You want to find a stolen one or have you got one that is hot and want to get rid of it?'

'No,' answered George. 'I . . . I have not got a stolen one. . . .'

'And you want to sell it?' said Mr. Williams matter-of-factly. He waved his pistol in George's direction and then put it on the floor. 'What makes you think I am dealing in stolen goods? Better watch your words, friend. People have gotten bullets in their bellies for lesser thoughts! Who *are* you? Who sends you here? And have you gotten the pearls with you?'

George could not suppress a smile. Williams laughed. 'Let's have a gargle and then you better tell me the whole story.' He produced a bottle of whisky.

'Luck to you!' he cried and swallowed his drink in one gulp. George lifted his glass, sipped and shuddered as the biting, near raw alcohol seared his throat. He put the glass down on the floor beside him and began.

'The police!' said Williams, when George had told him

all he thought he should know; 'the police are idiots. They want only money. Give them some, and you are all right. Three hundred dollars will make you the eternal friend of that bastard of a detective. Which would not stop him from shooting you down the next day if it suited him.' Gulping another drink, he added thoughtfully: 'Getting rid of the pearls is a bit tricky, but I know a way. Depends—what is in it for me.'

George suggested twenty per cent, Williams agreed on twenty-five with an immediate advance of $500. 'I have to safeguard my reputation and my standing,' he explained. George looked around the horrible room. In a corner lay a dead rat.

'What are the pearls worth?' asked Williams.

George told him he wanted $10,000.

'O.K. by me,' said Williams. 'Must be quite some pearls. Well, the higher we go, the more I get, so. . . .' He explained his plan of action. He would introduce George to a China-man who sold girls to the brothels of San Francisco's Chinatown. 'He runs a couple of "cow-yards" and he'll pay you the money you want. All Chinamen are crackers for pearls. Now you have still to produce a thief for your detective. Where are the pearls insured?'

George did not know. Williams shrugged and said he would find out. He would contact the insurance company and offer to retrieve the stolen pearls, then he would send the insurance assessor to the Chinaman, and collect the reward as well.

With the promise to return within an hour with $500 on account, George left the 'detective's' house and walked to his hotel, returning in good time to give Williams his money. He learned that a thief had already been lined up. 'For five hundred dollars,' said Williams, 'there are a thousand men in this city who would confess to anything short of murder, and be glad to have a rest in the pen for a while. And there are another thousand who, for a bottle of whisky, would swear that they saw the man doing it.'

Having put on a loud check shirt and a leather jacket, Williams led his client into the heart of the Barbary Coast.

The entire amusement district was lit up, a never ending stream of men of all ages, creeds and colours poured towards another night of crime and debauchery. The brothels and deadfalls, where customers were bashed over the head and rolled into the gutters on Kearny Street and Montgomery Street, had opened for business. The dance-halls with their 'pretty waiter girls' around Portsmouth Square did a roaring business; the concert saloons, the drinking dens, the melodeons and peep-shows, the gambling houses, the slave-girl cribs and the opium cellars in Chinatown were besieged by hundreds of miners and sailors, the scum of five continents, in a cacophony of earsplitting bands, bawling men and screeching women, while over all floated a miasma from unwashed bodies, burning kerosene, decaying fish, urine, disinfectant, and bad frying fat.

They reached Abe Warner's 'Cobweb Palace' near Meiggs's Wharf and entered the vast barn-like wooden building through a gap in its front. There was no door, for the 'Cobweb Palace' was open always, day and night. Compared with other Barbary Coast establishments, the 'Palace' was quiet. It was the haunt of sea captains, dive owners, brothel keepers, wealthy Chinese, and even businessmen from the city itself, lured by its potent hot toddy of whisky, gin and cloves.

There was no music and no dancing girls in the drinking room and no 'waiter girls'. The curtained booths on the first floor were there for private talks between men of business. The 'Cobweb Palace' had other attractions. Abe Warner had a weakness for spiders, and the entire place was completely covered in cobwebs, over the mirrors and walls, hanging from the ceilings, and spreading over the bars. They masked the collection of more than a thousand paintings of nude women which Abe had gathered in his thirty-five years of business. Everywhere stood cages of parrots and animals he had been given by his sea captains, while from the ceilings also hung walrus tusks and whale teeth, carefully engraved with patriotic scenes.

As slummers from Nob Hill often visited the 'Palace' to show visiting friends the sights of the Barbary Coast, a young man like George drew no particular attention. Williams led him up a wooden staircase to the first floor and into a booth, and a few minutes later Abe Warner appeared. Williams explained what they wanted and for a fee of another $500 Abe returned after an hour with a little Chinaman in a silken robe, his withered face adorned by a thin grey beard, and a round, lacquered cap on his head. Around this cap was carefully wound his plaited queue. With arms folded over his breast he bowed deeply to each of the men and watched them through half-closed eyes. He took the pearls from George, lifted them to his mouth and licked them with his tongue. He returned them to George with a bow and said in a high-pitched staccato voice: 'No bad pearnies . . . no bad pearnies at ann. Wei Chung Lei maybbee pay you two thousand donnars.'

It took all the persuasion of Abe Warner and Williams to raise the Chinaman's offer to $9,000. Each time the price went up, Wei Chung Lei took the pearls out of George's hands and tested them again. Finally he put them into his pocket and produced from beneath his robe nine small canvas bags, each holding $1,000 in gold. Without another word, bowing deeply, he left the booth and shuffled slowly out of the 'Palace'.

Williams smiled. 'The Chink is sure keen on pearls,' he said. 'Now, mister, take the loot. I take two sacks,' and he put two sacks into his pocket. Abe Warner returned with a bottle of champagne and three glasses. 'On the house,' he said and opened the bottle.

George was left with five sacks of gold. He put them in various pockets of his suit and shook hands with Warner, ready to leave. But Williams stopped him. 'Mister,' he said, 'I better come along with you. With those bulging pockets the Barbary Coast is no place to walk alone at night. And as we are now business partners, I would appreciate it very much if you tell me your name.'

They left the 'Cobweb Palace', walked up Pacific Street and past the 'Cowboy's Rest', the most notorious establishment on the Coast, owned by 'Cowboy Maggie', a lady who was her own bouncer and always carried a hickory bludgeon, a revolver and a stiletto. Williams delivered George at the door of his hotel. They shook hands. 'And,' said the 'detective' with a grin, 'go and see the Captain in the morning. If you want to produce the thief, come along to my place tomorrow.'

Captain O'Mahony received George with some surprise and suspicion when he was shown into his room at the City Hall.

'So you have come after all,' he said. 'Not, I suppose, with the pearls?'

George explained affably that he wanted to help catch the thief, and also to contribute to the Police Benevolent Fund. His $300 donation disappeared instantly into the pocket of the Captain, whose manner changed just as quickly. He produced a bottle of whisky from his desk and two glasses and poured drinks. George returned satisfied to his hotel.

In the afternoon he saw Williams again, still busy shooting rats. And next morning Patrolman Flaherty on his beat in Kearny Street arrested Augustus Svensborg, a Swedish beachcomber, who confessed to having stolen the pearls and produced four witnesses who had seen him on the train and hiding the pearls.

The insurance company announced that they had recovered the pearls in Chinatown. Williams gratefully accepted another $1,000 from George, who, $4,000 richer, decided it was time to see some of the high life of the city. He had had enough of the squalor and odours of the underworld. He deposited his money in the Bank of California and received a cheque-book for the first time in his life. Then he contacted a lady rejoicing at the return of her pearls.

They met at the Baldwin Hotel, at that time considered by Californians to have the most luxurious dining-room in the world, and afterwards went to a dance in the Pacific Club on Stockton. His partner was lovely, for round her neck she wore the pearls that had caused so much trouble.

George invited her back for a drink in his suite. When she left next morning, it was, once more, without her string of pearls.

This time the disappearance was not discovered until

the evening, because, semi-drunk, she had lurched along the corridor to the room she had taken in George's hotel, and slept the day through. The discreet Negro floor-maid who had put her to bed promised to see she was not disturbed. For the tip George had given her she would have promised to set fire to the hotel.

George, concerned with getting out of San Francisco as quickly as possible, decided that trains were too dangerous. Stations had telegraph offices. There was always the harbour, with clippers and paddle steamers, even propeller-driven ships, bound for every port in the world. He found a ship leaving at noon, drew his money from the bank, drove to the waterfront and was rowed out to the *Polynesia*, a German steamboat *en route* for Shanghai via Hawaii and the Philippines.

That evening he was deep in a game of poker with his money and his pearls safely locked up in the ship's strong room.

Chapter 5

The *Polynesia's* eight passengers were accommodated in two cabins on the boat-deck, an arrangement which did not please George Manolesco; he wanted privacy. He approached the purser and for fifty dollars the officer, a shrewd Saxonian, offered to exchange his own comfortable cabin for George's berth. The cabin, panelled in teak, was made homely with a mass of pictures—photogravures and paintings of scantily clothed females. Amid this display was, in glaring colours, the reproduction of an oil painting of Kaiser Wilhelm II in the blood-red uniform tunic of the Prussian hussars, his famous needle-sharp waxed moustache-ends pointing towards heaven. His Majesty looked disapprovingly at the lusty, provocative ladies surrounding him. Over the wash-basin was nailed an embroidered motto, 'Home Sweet Home', and between the two port-holes hung a masterpiece of the then so popular art of pyrography, announcing in intricate Gothic letters: 'Ehrlich währt am längsten' (Honesty lasts the longest), which produced an approving smile from George.

He settled down on the bed to indulge in his favourite relaxation, day-dreaming. During his stay in the United States he had seen much he disliked and he was not sorry to have left the country, although he would have preferred to return to Europe. When in later days he discussed the United States, George always said that Americans were raw and unpolished, lacking all European culture and sophistication. 'They are not subtle,' he would add. 'They hit themselves over the head with the eagerness with which other people take a bath—which they don't.'

By now the lady in the hotel in San Francisco had probably come back to life with a tremendous hangover and raised the alarm. Captain O'Mahony would have been informed and would try to take it out on Williams; but Williams— George was certain—was capable of looking after himself and would tonight celebrate the fury of the Captain of Detectives by killing more rats than usual. The insurance company would refuse to pay, when the full story was told. Well, then the lady's meat-packer husband back home in Chicago could always console her with another string of pearls. The main thing was that the right buyer be found by George, and not in such urgent circumstances as in San Francisco. He regretted that there was no Carcola around to help.

The ship had long passed through the Golden Gate when the gong sounded for dinner. It was now rolling a little, sea fog hid the brilliantly illuminated coastline; but from the lighthouse on the Farallon Islands a powerful beam pierced the darkness.

The small dining-room was decorated with another oil colour portrait of the Kaiser, this time in the golden armour of the Uhlans, looking sternly at his Empress Augusta, whose picture hung on the right. She wore a plain white blouse with a fish-boned collar, her homely face topped by high brushed hair with a huge bun. Under the massive pictures sat the Captain, presiding at dinner, a small man, overwhelmed in appearance by his gold-braided uniform; his narrow face carried a replica of his Emperor's moustache. George thought them distinctive and conferring a look of authority, and felt that he might benefit from such an adornment.

There were two young men with bull-necks and pink sabre scars on their flabby faces. They clicked their heels, bowed from the hips and announced in short staccato voices and in unison: 'With your permission, Baron von Slatten,' and sat down again with the precision of a well-trained variety act. George could think of nothing but a polite 'delighted'. The Captain explained that the two were the sons of the owner of the 1,700-ton *Polynesia*, sent by father on an educational tour round the world. George was convinced they would be a hit with the geisha-girls in Japan. His immediate left-hand neighbour at table was a smiling little Chinaman in correct European clothes, Mr. Fu Tu, Vice Consul of the Emperor in San Francisco. There were three middle-aged Americans on a sales trip to China. They were dressed completely alike, in green-grey travelling suits, brown boots and loosely bound cravats, and long, dark cigars stuck out of their breast pockets. They were engrossed in a discussion about the possibilities of selling telephones, sewing machines and wire fencing to the Chinese, but acknowledged the Captain's introduction by raising their glasses of beer with a resounding 'Howdy!'

Young Monsieur Challendier was on George's right hand, well dressed, black-haired, and clean-shaven. He shook George's hand enthusiastically, telling him how happy he was to have found someone among the Teutons to whom he could talk in his mother tongue. He came from Rouen and was travelling for pleasure after having inherited a fortune. 'I prefer these little cargo steamers to the huge passenger liners,' he said. 'They are so unpredictable and much more adventurous.'

George liked the youngster but could not suppress a feeling that he was *too* handsome, his smile *too* constant and assured. He was rather like the rich young men of the Café de l'Horloge in Paris, and George wondered if he really did prefer the austerity of a small boat to the high life on a liner, if he really travelled *just* for pleasure.

After dinner the passengers went into the diminutive smoking room and Monsieur Challendier suggested a game of cards. The two German students disapprovingly stood up, gathered their huge *steins* of beer and vanished back into the dining-room, clicking their heels and bowing to the company as they stood in the doorway. They considered playing cards with foreigners as unmanly and unworthy. Soon, deep manly voices could be heard singing martial songs and students' *lieder* to the accompaniment of a badly-tuned piano. Mr. Fu Tu declined politely, he did not play cards. 'Fan-tan, yes, with pleasure,' he said smiling, 'but cards are too simple!' But he remained as an onlooker.

So it was the three commercial travellers, Monsieur Challendier and George Manolesco who settled down to poker. The truth about Monsieur Challendier came to George within minutes—the cards were marked! Now he understood the gambler's face that would never drop it's smile, even if its owner lost.

George regarded the marked cards as a personal affront. Not that he had any objection to cheating—how could he? Nor that the young man tried cheating *him*—this was his privilege as a sharper. He objected to Monsieur Challendier's disregard for the intelligence of others by using marked cards. The three commercial travellers had noticed nothing, they probably never thought of being cheated. But to a serious gambler it was an insult. He had to teach the young man a lesson in what he called psychology. When it was George's turn to deal, to the great amazement of Monsieur Challendier, the card that was, for instance, clearly marked as the king of hearts, became the ten of diamonds. A queen changed into a two, and so forth. When the game ended, George had won the relatively small sum of $250 but had had a lot of fun. Challendier had not lost his gambler's smile. He accepted with pleasure an invitation to George's cabin, and a steward was dispatched to produce a bottle of champagne.

'My young friend,' said George (who was perhaps a year older than the Frenchman) in his most paternal and patronizing mood, 'you are a very good card player. But take my advice, and improve your style!'

Challendier looked up, surprised. 'What's wrong with my style?' he asked. 'Do you think that my markings are not good enough?' He said it smilingly and without the slightest blush.

George shrugged. 'Clumsy, my boy. They might be good enough for such people as the three Yanks, but have you ever tried them on a professional?'

'No,' said Challendier, slightly worried. 'Are you a professional?'

'Professional . . . what?' asked Manolesco. 'Gambler or sharper?'

'Are you?' insisted the young man. 'I would have sworn you are a gentleman.'

George laughed. 'But I *am* a gentleman,' he said. 'Why should a gentleman not know about cheating? Anyway, thank you for your compliment, but before you cheat you should always study the people you are going to play with.'

Challendier rubbed his chin thoughtfully. 'After all,' he said, 'I should be grateful to you and thank you for the interest you have taken in me. It is a thrilling experience to meet a . . . colleague. You know, sir, I ran away from Rouen, because there they never knew what a thrill was.'

George sipped his champagne. 'I am very glad,' he said, 'that I was able to thrill you. And if you wish, I am quite willing to play a solo game with you, if you care to add to your thrills . . . and experience.'

Challendier thought that over for a second or two and then accepted. The next evening an extraordinary gambling match took place in George's cabin. And to his utter surprise the cards were not marked. Instead the Frenchman showed an agility and quickness of his fingers that nearly equalled George's. Although he had not expected such expertise, George was delighted and enjoyed the cheating match as he never had enjoyed any card game before. It was a brilliant performance of two masters, unfortunately without any public to appreciate the finer points.

'We both tried our best,' recalled George, 'to outdo the other by any means, and as both knew the other was cheating, it was as equal as any honest game! We could as well have played without any tricks, and relied entirely upon the luck of the cards.'

When they added the chips in the end (they did not play for money), it turned out to be a draw. Challendier beamed and suggested that they should team up. Instead of cheating one another, they should combine forces and 'work' the other passengers for whatever the traffic would bear. It was not exactly in George's line, besides he doubted that the traffic would bear much. But when the smiling Mr. Fu Tu, with a wise, all-knowing face, mentioned to George a Chinese saying which George attributed to Confucius—'There is no foul play in a battle if you win', and nodded encouragingly when George switched a card at the evening's game, George smiled back and decided to play ball with Challendier.

When they were due to part some ten days later, Challendier suggested that George should accompany him. George was not interested. He thought of the meagre $400 he had won, of the boredom of a further long voyage and of the serious business ahead of him—disposing of that string of pearls.

*   *   *

A crowd of several hundred people greeted the *Polynesia* when she berthed behind a four-masted China clipper. Military music came from the landing stage, as the band of the Royal Hawaiian Household Music, under their Prussian conductor Herr Becker, began to play; marching tunes of the Prussian Army greeted the parcels of newspapers and mail that thudded on to the quay, and the crowd cheered as the boat was made fast. It was always a fiesta day when a boat arrived at the 'Cross Roads of the World'; Kanakas, Chinese migrants, Japanese servants, Malayan sugar-plantation workers, Indian craftsmen, beachcombers, sailors who had jumped their ships, and even a smattering of European and American settlers made up the crowd that enjoyed any break in the placid, eventless life of the Pacific paradise.

Suddenly the crowd fell into silence as down the gangplank stepped a tall young man in splendid white clothes, wearing a panama hat and glittering brown, lacquered shoes. In his hand he swung a cane with a silver handle and around his neck was loosely slung a silk kerchief of dark green. Monsieur George Manolesco arrived in grand style. Heedless of the stares, George took the only waiting carriage and was driven from the landing stage into town as Herr Becker lifted his baton and the band broke into the new, exciting melody 'The Star Spangled Banner'. The carriage brought George after a short drive to the Hawaiian Hotel on Alakea Street, opposite the imposing building of the former Royal Palace, and the premier establishment of its kind in Honolulu. Entering a garden crammed with flowers and exotic bushes, the carriage stopped under the huge *hau* tree at the

foot of the sweeping staircase to the first floor of the hotel.
A handful of Chinese houseboys slowly clattered down the
stairs, bowed politely, seized George's luggage and led the
way up to the reception room, where another Chinese boy
wandered aimlessly around with a broom. The Japanese
clerk behind the desk hissed a welcome. From behind a
bamboo curtain appeared the American owner of the hotel,
who swiftly appraised the trunks and cases of his new guest
and raised his price to five dollars a day for board and resi-
dence. His lean face creased with some effort into a smile
as he shook hands with George without removing the cold
cigar from the corner of his mouth.

The rooms were airy, the furniture rather sparingly distributed. In the bedroom stood a large, low bed, and a
washstand of iron flanked by two wicker chairs. The adjoining
sitting-room contained three more wicker chairs, a wobbly
iron garden table, and a chest of drawers with an unframed
mirror over it. Instead of a wardrobe, several long nails were
driven into the whitewashed walls, over which a few small
gaily-coloured lizards flickered. From both rooms the
balcony that ran round the hotel could be reached, but instead
of doors there were bamboo curtains rustling softly in the
mild breeze.

'No thievvies in Hawaii,' said the Chinese houseboy
smiling. 'Nobody steany in hoten. Boss no must worry . . .
can put thousand donnars, maybbee two thousand donnars
on chair. Is there tomorrow, and next tomorrow, and next
tomorrow . . . savvy?' George 'savvied' but slightly doubted
so much honesty, which he considered a dangerous provoca-
tion to anyone looking for money. But as there simply was
no place to hide his gold and banknotes and the hotel owner
also advised him to leave everything in the room, he left
his small leather case containing about $7,000 on the
rickety table in the sitting-room, put a few hundred dollars
and the string of pearls in his pocket and ordered a carriage
from the Japanese clerk. This arrived after about an hour.

George had by now gathered that in Honolulu time was
of no importance, nobody seemed to be in a hurry, neither the
skinny brown coachman, nor the few pedestrians they met,

mostly sauntering Chinese girls in white trousers. Even the small houses, brightly painted and set in gloriously blooming gardens, seemed asleep. Only an occasional ship's whistle from the harbour broke the silence. Then a clock struck the hour and a dignified bell from the horse-tram running to Waikiki beach could be heard. George dismissed the carriage in the city centre in Merchant Street, looked at the previous year's fashions in the window of the Emporium, discovered a banking house, the office of a shipping company and the Central Post Office, and walked down Kaarumani Street towards the river. Soon he found himself in an alley near the waterfront, with little houses of planks and bamboo leaning dangerously over into the narrow road. Here he nearly stumbled over a few tough-looking characters, sleeping dreamlessly in front of an *okolehau* drinking den, waiting to be collected by the 'runners' from the sailor's boarding-houses who would carry them aboard the man-hungry clippers. The whine and clatter of Chinese music and the wailing of Japanese arguments mingled with the shouts of the naked children of a dozen races who played in the gutters. Across the street two Portuguese sailors were involved in a heated discussion with a broad-shouldered Yankee beach-comber. When he saw George, the beachcomber felled the two sailors with a mighty blow each and crossed the road. Hands in pockets, he said: 'Say, mister, haven't you got an odd dollar somewhere tucked away, for which you have no use?' George gave him a silver dollar.

'Thanks, buddy,' grinned the other, 'and take my advice. Scram out of here. This is not a healthy neighbourhood for you, brother.'

'Well,' answered Manolesco, 'I do not like it much myself, but I am still alive. But . . . wait! Maybe we can do some kind of business together. Show me around if you have time to spare.'

The beachcomber laughed. 'Sure I have time to spare, mister. Time is cheap. What do you want to see? Cat houses, slave cribs or crooks? Take your pick. And tell me . . . what is in it for me?'

'Ten dollars,' suggested George.

'Ten dollars!' shouted the man.' Are you Rockefeller? For ten dollars I'll throw in a *nice* Chinese girl if you want. It's a deal, mister.'

George's new friend took him round Honolulu's 'little Barbary Coast', showed him opium dens and Chinese gambling houses, all the squalid side of paradise. He was a man with a striking sense of humour. He had come from the Fiji Islands and now lived in a wooden shack on Waikiki beach. 'Things became a little bit hot out in Fiji,' he explained. 'The English Navy got damned sore at us and suddenly started to clean up the blackbirders. We had three hundred niggers aboard when they intercepted us and set them free and chased us to the devil. Three hundred niggers at two hundred dollars apiece, can you imagine?'

He had intended to return to San Francisco and 'God's Own Country'. 'But then I forgot that the ship was sailing the same night from Honolulu, and got stuck. Slept it off at the beach and missed the boat.'

'And the next one?' asked Manolesco.

'I missed that too. At first I just lay on the beach and thought of the next boat. Then, after a while, I gave up thinking and just lay around in the sun. This little island gets you, mister.'

When they reached the 'Eastern Emporium' in a small cul-de-sac, its owner, Mr. Lei Hin Su, was half asleep on the pavement, sitting on a crate between two tables. One was laden with a weird mixture of souvenirs, little Buddhas, small vases, native trinkets, chop-sticks, dried fish and small sea animals. On the other table stood an orderly row of small straw boxes. George thought he was dreaming as he examined the contents: pearls, pearls on strings, mounted, loose, pearls of every size and form, ear-rings and necklaces, mounted on gold rings and pins, grey pearls, white pearls, rosy pearls, in a variety George had never seen before. Pearls, after diamonds, were George's greatest love. Before him lay a fortune in a wooden tray in a dirty alley.

The beachcomber answered George's unspoken question. 'The Chink buys them from the sailors, the beachcombers like me, the professional thieves who pass through here. They all need hard cash. I thought Su's little collection might interest you.'

Until then the fat Chinaman sitting on the crate had not moved. He did not flicker an eyelid when George took some pearls from the baskets to examine them. They were faultless. To sell his stolen pearls here, for next to nothing, could be only foolish; but perhaps he could *buy* some pearls cheap enough to make a real profit on resale when at last he got back to Europe. He picked a selection from the baskets and asked the price. The Chinaman glanced sleepily at the outstretched hand and murmured: 'Maybbee five hundred donnars?'

George could not believe his ears. He had estimated their lowest value at about $10,000, but the beachcomber would not let him buy even at $500. 'You can get him down to three hundred,' he said and started bargaining. It ended in agreement at $400. By now the street, narrow and small, was crowded by an admiring crowd of idlers, seamen and plain thugs. As George put his hand in his pocket for money the beachcomber stopped him. 'Do not pay him now. Don't show your money. Go to your hotel and return with the cash in an envelope. Most people around here think the easiest way to rob a man is to kill him first!'

'And what about you?' asked Manolesco.

'Me?' said the beachcomber. 'I could have bashed you over the head a dozen times, but you pay me, mister. Why should I go to the trouble and knock you on the nob? I am an honest man, sometimes anyway, and all I want is to return to my beach after the excitement on a hot day like this.' He guided George through the maze of alleys and waited for his return in a bar not far from the hotel. In his rooms George found to his utter surprise that the leather case was untouched. He put $400 in an envelope and made his way to the beachcomber's bar.

Later he told the story of his Honolulu adventure to his second wife Pauline, again and again, for to him it was an extraordinary experience to satisfy a weakness for pearls by buying them. He always said: 'It was real and honest business,' and added, 'I could not exclude the possibility that the Chinaman and the American were working hand in hand and that the bargain offer of the pearls was only to make me show my money, which was a pure business risk.'

Within a few minutes the deal with Su was completed, the pearls carefully wrapped in a square of silk, and George and his companion returned to the city centre. Here George quietly handed his companion fifty dollars. 'Mister,' said the man staring at the treasury note, 'now I know you must be Rockefeller. This buys a lot of whisky. It's been a pleasure knowing you. If you want anything else, name it. Come out to Waikiki Beach and just whistle for yours truly.'

George felt that the results of his first day in Hawaii were not too bad. With the San Francisco pearls he now had gems worth at least a million French francs. He made up his mind to return to Europe at once, feeling a sudden longing for the life of Paris, the bright lights on the boulevards, not to mention the money waiting at Machinelle's or Carcola's. Supper in the hotel, Hawaiian style, only spurred his decision. Chicken stewed in coco-nut milk, seaweed and shrimps . . . this was no menu for George Manolesco, connoisseur of Durand's *Soufflé truffé à la Reine Antoinette*. After a night of mosquito bites, he rushed to buy a ticket on the first outward passenger steamer, which was leaving for Vancouver Island in British Columbia in three days. The hotel proprietor was sorry to lose five dollars a day and tried to persuade George to stay longer. He rode with him to Waikiki Beach and even introduced him to the Beach Club, where a select colony of sugar planters and government advisers lolled on the shady *lanai* of the wooden club-house, systematically destroying their livers with iced drinks. George was adamant. He was already mentally strolling along the Champs-Elysées on a sunny afternoon, pausing for a chat with Corporal Elias, who guarded the Arc de Triomphe. The few tawdry gems proudly worn by some of the women at the Beach Club totally failed to interest him.

As usual, half the population saw George off from the waterfront as Bandleader Becker with his Royal Musicians played farewell tunes, including the sad German "Muss I denn . . .' (Must I leave this lovely town . . .). George stood at the railing and waved at the girls in short skirts throwing flowers after the boat as it slowly glided along the narrow channel between the mudbanks, before the open sea. When Diamond Head disappeared, he went to his cabin. Here were some souvenirs from the Cross Roads of the World: A small Hawaiian goddess in wood, and a heavy bronze Buddha in whose hollowed-out belly lay his pearls. The Buddha rested, for all to see, on a small shelf under the port-hole.

Apart from a few games of poker in the smoking room, so dull that he did not even bother to cheat, he passed most of the ten days alone in a deck chair, dreaming of Paris. From Vancouver he travelled by train to New York, shipped on the new French luxury steamer *La Normandie*, and arrived at Le Havre on June 24, 1894, two years after he had left it, and more or less at the moment that President Carnot was assassinated in Lyons.

*   *   *

Paris that night was a strange city. The Gare St.-Lazare was jammed with National Guards, dozens of police patrolled the streets, a great search was under way for the murderers of the President.

George drove to the Hotel Continental in the rue Rivoli through mournful streets, with lights extinguished and draped with black veils, flags at half-mast.

That very night he went to Machinelle. He found the fat Italian, despite the late hour, still in his little office behind the Bastille. Machinelle nodded, as if George had been there only the previous day. 'Hallo,' he said. 'Sit down and tell me what I can do for you.'

George showed him the pearls. 'Good stuff,' proclaimed Machinelle. 'But I cannot buy them now. They have raided my place twice during the afternoon, not becuse they realize I am a . . . er . . . fence, but just because I am an Italian. They think that all the Italians in France are connected with the stabbing in Lyons. You should not have come here, for they watch this place.'

'They have nothing against me,' said George.

'Oh,' exclaimed Machinelle as he returned the pearls to George, 'you seem to have forgotten your little holiday in the Prison Gaillon. The *flics* would be only too pleased to put you back. Anybody who ever served a jail sentence is an automatic suspect, as you know. And secondly, why the hell can you not keep your mouth shut? Why must you boast of your cleverness? Why did you tell "Le Pecheur" about Fontana's and Cartier? I know, I know,' he continued, lifting both hands as George wanted to say something; 'even in a bloody jail you wanted to be somebody. But "Le Pecheur" is no father confessor, and has shot his mouth off. Proud to know you . . . the Great Manolesco! You have made yourself quite a reputation in the underworld—and with the police! You are a famous man, George . . . so famous that you'd better scram out of Paris as quickly as you can. There is a reward of five thousand francs for you!'

It was a terrible shock to George. Here he was, with a price on his head, with a veritable fortune in gems in his pockets, and registered in a hotel under his own name! He was almost inclined to believe the saying that pearls are unlucky. He left the office by a back door and walked slowly to his hotel. He had thought of abandoning the hotel and vanishing but felt this was unworthy of the 'famous George Manolesco'. A Manolesco did not run away from the stupid *flics*! To hell with the *flics*! Besides he considered it unlikely that the police would look for him in an hotel like the Continental. He slept well and was up at six, paid his bill and took a carriage to the Gare de Lyon, a few minutes before the police arrived at the hotel for their daily routine check of the guest register. He walked coolly past police and National Guards in the station, following a porter loaded down with his luggage. He planned to go to Carcola in Marseilles but he did not dare take the direct route to the South via Lyons, and instead boarded the express for Bordeaux, reserving a complete compartment for himself by the simple process of buying four first-class tickets and giving a princely tip to the conductor. He reached Bordeaux late in the evening and checked in at the Grand Hôtel de

Bordeaux—in the Grande Place, facing the theatre—signing the register as George Mercadente, his middle name. In the adjoining Café du Théâtre he ordered a dinner which made the headwaiter stare in admiration, and chose his wine with such assurance and knowledge that the *sommelier* felt obliged to congratulate Monsieur and to enter into a lengthy discussion on the differences of the good wines of Burgundy and Bordeaux. George was only sorry to dine alone: a beautiful female companion would have made it a perfect evening.

'The saints must have heard my silent prayer,' insisted George later, for, as he finished his soup, a carriage stopped outside the terrace and he saw Violetta.

To describe Violetta as sensational in appearance would be an understatement. She wore a long sweeping skirt and wasp-waisted jacket of the same material, and a wide-brimmed black hat tied under her chin with a black velvet ribbon, and from beneath this her flaming red hair stood out vividly. So, George noticed as she bent forward in stepping down from the carriage, did her generous bosom which was barely covered by her low white blouse and imposed a grave strain on the severely-tailored jacket. It was clear that the coachman could not understand what she was saying and George was quickly to the rescue. Jumping from his table he ran to the coach. Violetta explained in bad French that she was a Hungarian. Could Monsieur perhaps speak German? George could and in a few minutes she was being escorted to a suite next to George's own. As he kissed her hand at the door, the suggestion of a glass of champagne in half an hour was smilingly accepted. Sitting on a scarlet plush sofa Violetta explained that she was a music hall artiste *en route* for Spain, but with a week to spare to see the sights of southern France. Also, she added, she was lonely.

George thought it over swiftly and dispassionately. She was desirable enough. If the French police were looking for him, the last people they would suspect were a pair of lovers travelling casually from town to town, from hotel to hotel. Leading her chastely to her bedroom door, George bowed respectfully over her hand and offered to escort her for some days.

The next afternoon they reached Toulouse and took a two-bedroomed suite at the Hôtel Tivollier in the Place du Capitole. As distinguished strangers they dined at Tortoni's in the Allée Lafayette and George ordered the town's famous speciality, *paté de foies de canard aux truffes*. He stayed polite, gentlemanly and a trifle reserved. But Violetta did not waste time. That night, sipping champagne in their sitting-room, she expressed surprise that George had never seen her on the stage, for she had created a sensation in Paris. 'I was travelling in America,' he explained, and she rose from her chair and said laughingly: 'But then you must see me dance . . . yes . . . I will give you a private performance. One of my dances that set all Paris demanding more and more !'

There was no music, she softly hummed the rhythm and went into the first steps of her dance. But the long, sweeping train of her evening dress made a Czardas quite impossible! She tried lifting her skirt, first with one hand and then with two, but short of wrapping it around her neck, there was clearly no solution here. She stopped, looked for a second at George as he sat watching her, and with a swift angry movement ripped with each hand at the bodice of her gown. It split almost to the waist and once again she ripped till she had torn it past her hips. She stood motionless in front of George as the gown slithered slowly to the floor, to leave her clad only in a short camisole that covered her from the waist to just above her knees, her long legs startlingly erotic in their black silk stockings. Without a word she started to perform once more, her bare heavy breasts swaying and jigging with the wild movements of the Hungarian national dance.

Excited despite himself, George rose to his feet and caught her in his arms to lead her to the sofa.

'Cool down my beautiful Puszta girl,' he murmured, 'cool down . . . and you will do it better without these few last bits of clothes!'

Monsieur and Madame Mercadente arrived in Marseilles two days later and there George made a discovery. On examining his bronze Buddha, he found about a dozen pearls

missing. As Violetta slept peacefully that night, he retrieved
the pearls from her handbag and, before she woke in the
morning, he went down to the hotel writing-room and
wrote a note:

> Chérie,
>   One is enough. I am strongly opposed to overpaying for
> any kind of favours, even if they be as nice as yours!

He enclosed one pearl in the envelope, paid the bill,
gave orders that Madame was not to be disturbed before
the afternoon, when she would catch the Barcelona train, and
took a carriage to the rue de Mont de Piété.

'George!' cried Carcola. 'I had given you up! So you
haven't been arrested?'

'Why should I?' said George smiling, and told him of his
little adventure with the Hungarian dancer. Carcola roared
with laughter. 'I don't know, George,' he said, 'but wherever
you turn up something happens.'

Carcola, after some stiff bargaining, agreed to pay
400,000 francs for all the pearls.

'Chicken feed,' said George. 'You can do better. After all
I have carried them half around the world.'

Carcola shook his head. 'Have a heart, George,' he said.
'It is nearly all the cash I have. You have completely cleaned
me out,' and he opened his wall safe.

'The things I do for you,' smiled George as he put the
crisp new thousand-franc notes in an envelope and stuffed it
in his pocket. He was not worried about Carcola and was
sure that the sly old fox had customers already lined up, and
a certain substantial profit. 'I feel so frightfully sorry for
you,' he said finally, 'that I will buy you supper, with onion
soup.'

During the long meal Carcola, well informed as ever, told
with some glee how 'La Trevolle' had been involved in two
scandals, so enormous, even for Paris, that she had gone
with her 'long suffering husband' to their estate in the south.
The Trevolles had one villa near Geneva in Switzerland
and others scattered along the Mediterranean coast from
Italy to the Spanish border. Near dawn George collected his

luggage from Carcola's office, drove to the Nouvelle Gare
and took a train to Cannes. With 400,000 francs in his
pocket he was now prepared to fulfil his life's ambition to be
accepted by Europe's very rich as one of themselves.

It did not, however, work out that way. Certainly he was
at once accepted into the set of the Côte d'Azur but he could
not resist the gambling tables. This time he tried his luck
at roulette, and found to his regret that there was no way
of cheating the machine. Within three weeks he had lost
nearly all his money and had not enough to pay his formidable
hotel bill. Paradoxically, it was difficult to pick up money
in a society which lost hundreds of thousands of francs nightly.
The grand dukes, the duchesses, the German industrialists,
the Italian politicians and the South American cattle breeders
gave no parties that he could gate-crash. He had to revert
to his old methods in Athens, Vienna and Paris, and steal
from shops and hotels. He never stole in his own hotel and
tried to be as careful as possible, but the run of thefts could
not go unnoticed, specially by the Press, who called it a 'new
kind of thievery, by a robber without nerve'.

Then a journalist recalled the notorious robber of hotels
and jewellers some four years previously in Paris, whose
name was George Manolesco. Monsieur George Mercadente
smiled at first, but then police said they were sure that the
thief must be well known, probably was a visitor to the
hotels he robbed, as he never broke into a room, used a false
key, or even the newly invented Quistiti (a universal instru-
ment designed by a master thief for hotel theft and which,
inserted into any lock, could be expanded to the size of the
proper key, and was thus supposed to open any door).
George decided it would be better to leave the Riviera and
try his luck elsewhere. He travelled to Baden Baden in the
Black Forest, then at the height of its season and full of
international society.

It was here that George practised and brought to perfection his technique of robbing lonely and, if possible,
beautiful women. 'Nobody,' he said, 'has ever counted how
many respectable lonely women there are in the luxury hotels
of the great Spas, looking for the excitement life has denied

them. In some cases their husbands are dead, leaving useful fortunes, or they cannot travel with them because they are too busy making the fortunes. Such ladies are so grateful for a little attention, friendliness, and perhaps, love, and count not the price of a necklace or a diamond brooch.'

At Spa in Belgium he won 50,000 francs at baccara, and lost it at the roulette tables in Monte Carlo. He was arrested in Zürich but they had to let him go. In Vienna he registered at the Hôtel de France, without attracting the attention of the police, whose headquarters were next door. By the simple process of lending some money to a young officer of the Imperial Guard, who had lost all at the tables, he was introduced at the exclusive Jockey Club, and became a member.

The day before he left Vienna, he made the acquaintance of an elderly gentleman in the hall of the hotel. He had an open, friendly face, bushy eyebrows and a drooping grey moustache. His clothes were so obviously country—a green Loden jacket and corduroy trousers too short to cover fully his strong brown military boots—that George classified him as a landowner from the remote provinces of Austria. He was right about his profession, but not of his nationality. He turned out to be a Romanian with an estate near Craiova, and very pleased to meet a countryman so obviously a gentleman of standing and means as Monsieur Mercadente. Having finished his business in Vienna, he was pleased to accept an invitation from George for a Vienna coffee on the terrace of the Sacher Hotel, and later dined with his new friend at the Meisl & Schadn restaurant.

He had introduced himself as Lahovary, and it took George half an hour to recognize the name Lahovary as that of an old noble Romanian family, slightly impoverished lately, but still quite a well-known name in his country.

'So,' he said. 'You are *Prince* Lahovary?'

The old gentleman smiled friendlily. 'I wondered how long it would take you to place the name. Anyway, let's drop the Prince and there is no need to address me as Your Highness. Here, I am just plain Mr. Lahovary . . . you see, it makes things less complicated and travelling cheaper.' And when

George nodded rather unconvinced and looked doubtfully at the Prince, he added: 'It saves me from seeing all my cousins and uncles at the Court, which, believe me, is a rather costly business. I don't bother them and they don't bother me. As Mr. Lahovary I need not change for dinner. Thank God . . . for I haven't got a tail coat.'

In the evening George suggested a little excursion to Grinzing, and 'Mr.' Lahovary accepted. They took a carriage to the suburb and started on a gay tour of the Heuriger inns, to taste the young wine.

At the third inn and the fifth litre of young wine, Lahovary had told George all about himself and they were on the very best of terms. 'Monsieur Mercadente!' said Prince Lahovary, 'you are an awfully good feller. I tell you what. You must come and visit me in Craiova when you come again to Romania.'

George promised. 'Fine,' said the Prince. 'I accept your promise. And by the way, what is your Christian name?' George told him.

'George?' cried the Prince. 'I am George, too. Now . . . that is really a wonderful coincidence.' And hiccupping lustily, he suggested they drop all formalities and call each other by their Christian names. 'If only to confuse the others,' he said, 'if George calls George, 'George'!' he laughed with drunken glee.

At six o'clock in the morning Prince Lahovary was so tired that he scarcely could keep his eyes open, but he was not completely drunk. He remembered that he had a reservation on the Balkan Express, which left Vienna's East Station at eight. He told George so.

George ordered coffee and small salami sausages. 'I'll take you to your train,' he said. 'Leave everything to George, George!'

'Sure!' said the Prince. 'George . . . you are my best friend. I trust you. I don't know what George would do without George,' and slapped George on the back. 'You dump me on my train,' he continued. 'Get my luggage from the hotel. Eight twenty-two, my boy . . . don't forget the time,' and went to sleep.

George after having drunk two cups of hot, strong coffee was as near sober as could be expected, sober enough to call a carriage and, with the help of a cellar-man, to load his sleeping friend into it. They arrived at the Hôtel de France shortly after seven o'clock, and George, letting his friend sleep in the carriage, went up to Lahovary's room to collect his luggage. Two small suitcases waited on a luggage stand, packed but open. They contained nothing which would have interested George, a spare pair of shoes, linen, another suit, everything rather crumpled and pushed into the bags. Prince Lahovary was not a very tidy man, it seemed. George snapped shut the locks of the cases and looked around for things forgotten.

On the dressing-table near the bed he found a small leather case and opened it. It contained a few hundred Kroner in banknotes, a bundle of Romanian money, and a batch of papers. He counted the money and found it too little to bother with. The Prince was travelling on a shoe-string and would need the money during his journey. He looked through the papers and a sudden thought struck him. Here were documents which would give him a new and excellent identity: a bundle of four letters addressed to Prince Lahovary, a stamped permission from the authorities to pass the border, a summons from the land registry to appear in a dispute about a piece of land, and a receipted bill for a plough delivered to the estate. There was also a passport, the first Romanian passport George had ever seen, but that did not interest him. He did not need a passport, no one ever asked for it unless one wanted to go to Russia. And that George had not in mind.

He took the papers, returned the passport and the money to the small leather case, rang the bell, had the luggage taken down to the carriage and went to the reception office to pay Lahovary's bill. It was a ridiculously small sum, and he paid it out of his own pocket.

He tipped the porter who took the luggage to the waiting carriage and, with his friend still sleeping soundly, he drove to the station. With the help of a porter he 'dumped' Prince Lahovary in a second-class compartment in the direct coach to Cernauti, returned the ticket and the reservation slip to the Prince's pocket where he had found it, and began trying to wake him up.

He succeeded five minutes before the train left. When the Prince returned more or less to his senses, George gave him the paid hotel bill, his small leather case and his luggage, and said good-bye. 'George,' moaned the Prince, 'how can I ever thank you? My headache is killing me . . . but it was wonderful, really wonderful,' and fell back asleep again.

George stood on the platform until the train had left the station. Then he returned to the Hôtel de France, packed his own luggage, paid his bill and drove to the West Station to catch the morning train to Switzerland, in the opposite direction.

H.H. Prince Lahovary appeared for the first time in public a fortnight later in Baden Baden where he robbed an American of $25,000. Then the rich landowner from Romania started his great career as a super thief on the Côte d'Azur, specializing mainly in the gems of neglected women. He was soon known in the Grand Hotels as a gentleman of impeccable standing, below-stairs as the only gentleman of *real* standing . . . and as the perfect Don Juan. He was now at the height of his reputation as a generous spender, as the ideal guest, a real Prince with his perfectly maintained moustaches and embroidered silk night-shirts, the perfect image of noble blood; while in the underworld they talked of George Manolesco, the arch-thief who could never be caught.

Chapter 6

The wide, crimson-carpeted hotel corridor was empty and hushed. Lights were turned down, and George peering cautiously out of a bedroom door could only just distinguish the long line of pairs of shoes neatly placed outside each white door. He turned and nodded encouragingly to the woman standing behind him, murmured a few gallant platitudes and kissed her hand mechanically as she slipped past him, with the shy smile of the woman who has just left a strange man's bed, to rejoin her husband in her own suite.

She ran silently along the corridor on stockinged feet, shoes in one hand, the train of her evening gown firmly clutched in the other. Where the corridor was crossed by another she stopped and looked cautiously right and left, then turned to glance back the way she had come. He still stood in the open doorway and now he half raised his hand in a tired salute of reassurance. As she disappeared round the corner, he closed his door noiselessly. Not that anyone would hear. At two in the morning in Nice's Hôtel Angle-terre practically nobody was awake; even the servants on night duty would be sleeping downstairs in the easy chairs under the potted palms. But the etiquette of gallantry demanded a show of discretion, an air of secrecy to add spice to the illusion of romance.

George caught a glimpse of himself in the full-length mirror of his room and yawned, distorting his outrageously handsome face, of classic Grecian style. The figure was growing slightly portly from the good food of Europe's top hotels in an era when food was taken seriously. He stroked his thick black Kaiser Wilhelm moustache and momentarily admired himself—his dark, brilliant and flashing eyes, raven, slightly waved hair, and the really beautifully-kept white hands which—except in jail—had never done a stroke of hard manual work in their lives. He yawned again, for he was sick and tired of the whole procession of romantic 'adventures' with the neglected wives of rich society lay-abouts. Once, true, it had been exciting, but now it was pure (if one could use such an adjective) cold, calculated routine, with little mental or sexual excitement, and not even much risk.

For him there was no longer need for elaborate and complicated preparations or painstaking research into the status of an intended victim. A glance at her, at her husband and at her jewels—most especially at her jewels—was sufficient to tell him if he had picked the right person to contribute to the ever-growing expenses of Prince Lahovary. The rest was easy . . . and so dull!

He locked his door and went to the wall to pull the silk cord that would extinguish the big crystal chandelier in the middle of the room. The gas jets fluttered, hissed, and went out. The room was in darkness and he waited until his eyes grew accustomed to it. He wished he were far away, on a small island off the beaten track, where there were no Grand Hotels and no dissatisfied, adventure-hungry wives with fortunes around their necks, whose husbands were drunkards, *roués* and wasters who did not care what their women did or with whom they did it as long as they were left alone to squander the dowries at the gaming tables.

'We are honoured to know you, Prince Lahovary,' the victim would say after the introduction by a mutual acquaint-ance or by an eager *maître d'hôtel* anxious to please such a generous guest as His Highness.

'It is entirely my pleasure,' he would answer with easy grace and bend to kiss Madame's hand.

Then would follow more meaningless phrases while the husband began to fidget and steal glances at the clock. His Highness knew precisely what was going to follow, for he had timed the meeting perfectly. He would suggest a drive in his carriage and supper at the Café de Paris.

'How lovely!' she would cry, and smile at her husband who was not over-enthusiastic since it was but ten minutes to opening time in the gambling rooms. 'Unfortunately I have a rather important appointment tonight,' Husband would say, a little stiffly. 'You must excuse me.'

'And Madame?'—a questioning look at her. 'Surely Madame does not participate in Monsieur's business affairs?'

Madame did not participate in them. So, with the gracious permission of Monsieur, it was agreed that Madame would go for the drive and Monsieur would join them later, after his appointment.

This was the almost invariable first act of the comedy.

George chuckled in the darkness. The acquisition of the title 'Prince Lahovary' definitely was one of his better achievements. In the closing years of the nineteenth century and in a society of wealthy idlers, inordinately impressed by any title, he was now a rich landowner from Transylvania and in appearance and manners he was, to tell the truth, a distinct improvement on the genuine Prince. He was elegant in bearing, he behaved like a real nobleman, he was generous with tips. Distant and aloof when necessary, he could be particularly friendly and charming when it suited him, and he would always be pointed out by waiters, chambermaids and near-drooling *chefs de reception* as the ideal illustrious guest. He entered totally into his role; he *was* Prince Lahovary, even to himself, every second of the day, including the moment when he put on his night-shirt with the red crown embroidered on the left breast.

Now, still chuckling, he walked carefully through the darkened room towards the huge marble fireplace in the corner. From a small side table he lifted some papers and books and felt for the necklace hidden beneath them. Then he sank into the overstuffed armchair and slowly slid the string of pearls to and fro through his hands, his sensitive fingers appraising their smoothness and size. Carcola would love these for his Oriental customers!

By now his enamoured companion of the evening would have discovered the loss of her pearls. She would no doubt remember that as George had tenderly and expertly undressed her in the darkened room and guided her to the bed, his hands had fluttered gently over her shoulders and breasts, had felt the necklace nestling between them.

'We will place the necklace here, on this little table, that it may not be damaged, my lovely, passionate one,' he had whispered. And now, what could she do? So long as her husband did not discover the loss that night all was well. The husband, if Manolesco guessed correctly, was sleeping off his drink and losses and in no condition to notice Madame's stealthy return to their room. In the morning no doubt she would find some excuse to talk to George and, so embarrassed, ask if he had found the pearls in his room. It was a pity, but she would be disappointed. He had already notified the hotel of his very early departure and his bill would be ready long before Madame was down. It would be difficult for her to explain the loss to a spouse with a tremendous hangover.

But why should *he* worry? She was not only beautiful, but also quite intelligent. He was certain she would find a good explanation. They always did.

He put the pearls into the pocket of his silken dressing-gown, leaned back and closed his eyes. The room was hot and his visitor's perfume still lingered on the air. The windows were closed to keep out the mosquitoes. George fell asleep in the chair.

He woke with a start and took several seconds to remember where he was. He did not know how long he had slept, but the room was still in darkness. Then, wide awake, he realized that he had heard a noise and he listened, motionless. There it was again. A scarcely audible scratching from the french windows which led to a small balcony overlooking the sea.

A click followed as the window was opened. The heavy drapes swayed slightly in the draught and were then noiselessly pushed aside. Against the grey morning sky, announcing the dawn, appeared the figure of a man. He stood still, silhouetted in the frame of the high window, and listened. After a few moments he stepped over the sill and entered, letting the curtain fall into place behind him. Again the room was in darkness. George, hidden in the deep arm-chair, heard the intruder shuffle over the carpet. He listened with professional interest.

With cat-like sureness the visitor avoided any obstacles. Suddenly a match flared. Manolesco saw a man standing by the rumpled bed, shaking his head as he found it empty. The match went out. Another match was used to light the candle on the night table. The man listened intently and as everything seemed quiet, bent over the night table and care-fully opened the drawer. George held his breath. Fascinated he watched the man take his gold watch and chain, his pocket-book bulging with banknotes, and a handful of silver and gold coins and put them into his pocket. He closed the drawer and blew out the candle. Then he began his way back through the darkness to the window.

For George it was a completely new experience to be the victim of a theft instead of being at the receiving end.

Waiting until the man had reached the window bay, he felt along the wall for the light-cord, and pulled. The gas hissed out of the jets in the chandelier, caught the tiny flame from the pilot light, and the room was brilliantly lit. At the same time, George spoke, in a cheerful, firm voice with a mocking undertone. 'Just a second, my friend. Stand still and raise your hands!'

The intruder turned round as he slowly raised his hands above his head. In the right hand he held a short thick bludgeon.

'Drop the cosh,' commanded George. 'And then you can lower your arms.'

The man obeyed him silently. He was a small fellow with dark hair under a black cap. He had on a well-worn blue serge jacket and striped trousers. George sized him up as a footman or a valet, perhaps a house porter. Around his neck he had slung his shoes on a string, and he was wearing blue silk stockings of the latest fashion. His complexion was the brownish-yellow of the southerner. He regarded his captor with deep, dark, steady eyes and without the slightest sign of embarrassment or fright. For a moment he glanced down at the cosh.

'Don't be a fool,' said the mocking voice. 'Violence is for idiots only. Use your brain, my friend. You do not look like a fool!'

The man started to say something, but George shook his head. 'You can explain later,' he said smiling. 'First hand over the things you have taken out of my drawer.'

There was no answer and the man made no effort to obey.

'All right,' said George. 'I give you exactly half a minute to do as I say. If by then my property is not on this little table I will pull the bell and raise the alarm. And do not make any foolish moves, my friend. I have a gun in my pocket and have you covered.' He moved his finger menacingly in the pocket.

The man stared at the movement and grunted. 'Will you let me go when I return them to you?' he asked in a surprisingly well-modulated, cultivated voice.

'We can have all our arguments later,' said George. 'You have exactly twenty seconds left.' The finger in the pocket moved upwards.

'But Monsieur . . .' said the burglar.

'Ten seconds,' with a glance at the bell-cord.

The man shrugged and slowly took from his pockets the watch and chain, the pocket-book, and the silver and gold coins and put them on a table by the wall.

George nodded acknowledgement and smiled. He was beginning to enjoy the little man's visit and had taken rather a liking to him.

'What else have you got in your pockets?' he asked.

'Nothing of yours,' was the defiant answer.

'Let us see,' said George. 'Empty your pockets.'

'Monsieur!' cried the man.

'Put them on the table,' continued George.

'Have a heart!' pleaded the man.

Manolesco touched the bell-cord. 'I am waiting,' he said.

A minute later various objects were laid out on the table. Two small gold watches, one gold chain, a diamond bangle, a small case of banknotes, a pearl tie-pin. George took up the various items one by one and studied them with interest.

'Not too bad a collection,' he said finally. 'A good job you did tonight.' He felt very superior and in his most patronizing mood. His visitor grunted again. 'However,' continued George, picking the diamond bangle up again and holding it in the air. 'You are not careful enough, my friend. You have been done! These are no diamonds. Very good imitations, Italian paste . . . with the gold mounting you might be able to get ten francs for it . . . if you can find a buyer.'

'That's not true!' exclaimed the man.

'I am afraid it is,' said George and threw the bangle to the burglar. 'If you don't believe me, go over to the mirror and try to cut it.'

'I'll be damned,' said the man after a few minutes. 'And she the widow of a Paris banker. Paste! She has money to burn.'

George shrugged. 'Such is life,' he said smiling. 'We all make mistakes. Probably she has got her real jewels in a bank safe, and wears only the imitations.' He pointed to an easy chair opposite. 'Sit down, my friend. No need to get angry over a little error like that. Relax, take it easy. Would you like a drink?'

The burglar did not show any surprise at the invitation to drink with his intended victim. His answer was calm and polite. 'Thank you very much, Monsieur. I would very much like to have one.'

George took a bottle and two glasses from a sideboard and poured two generous drinks. His visitor accepted his glass with a slight bow, smelled the contents and then took a sip.

'This is very good stuff,' he said with great conviction and respect, and lifted his glass. 'Your good health, Monsieur.' He swallowed it in one gulp.

George had never heard of a burglar who had been caught in the act then toasting the health of the victim. He raised his glass in return and answered: 'Your health, my friend. I am very glad you like the drink.'

'Very much, Monsieur,' nodded the visitor. 'Armagnac?'

'Yes.'

'I would say, 1860 Armagnac.'

'Precisely,' answered George.

'A very good year, 1860.'

George put down his glass and laughed. 'You seem to be a connoisseur, my friend,' he said.

His visitor shrugged. 'One has to be,' he answered modestly. 'I lived for a time in the Gascogne, where they make the finest Armagnac.'

'You surprise me,' said George affably. 'What is your name?'

He received no answer.

George shook his head disapprovingly. 'Come, come,' he said. 'You disappoint me. Anyone would like to know the name of a man who has such knowledge of liquor as you have. Besides, I always like to know who I am talking to. Now that we are on such friendly terms, don't disturb the amicable atmosphere of our meeting. What is your name?'

'Pellicio,' said the man. 'Franzesco Pellicio, at your service.'

'Italian?'

'No,' was the proud answer. 'Corsican.'

'A Corsican!' exclaimed George. 'Like all great Frenchman.'

He settled down again in the easy chair. In a few moments he had extracted the information that Franzesco Auguste Pellicio had acquired Italian nationality when in the service of Prince Colonna, the Mayor of Rome, and was then known as Pellicia. On his return to France he reverted to the Corsican spelling.

'Can I go now?' asked Pellicio.

George shook his head. 'Stay in your chair and keep quiet for a few minutes, until I have made up my mind.'

An idea had just occurred to him. It was not a new idea, he had played with it for a long time and always dropped it for lack of opportunity. If his judgement of men did not deceive him, this was the moment he had waited for. He looked at his uninvited visitor who sat hunched back in his chair, a defiant expression on his face.

'I know well how you feel, Pellicio,' said George. 'You have bungled a good job by being very careless and thus have spoiled your entire evening's entertainment. Have you been in service?'

'Yes. I got the sack.'

'Why?'

'Why do you want to know? My face did not fit.'

'I see,' nodded George. 'Have another drink, and let us discuss matters from a practical point of view. Have you ever been arrested by the police?'

'Never,' said Pellicio.

'Excellent,' beamed George. 'Never been caught before?'

'No. This is the first time I have slipped. I was very tired.'

Not a word of remorse. No protestation that he would never do it again! A proud little man.

George slowly stood up and walked across the room towards the windows, deliberately turning his back to the burglar. He pulled the heavy drapes aside and the rising sun lit the room. He went back and looked at his watch, still on the small table. It was 4.30 a.m. In four hours his train would leave for Marseilles.

Pellicio had not stirred, nor made any attempt to retrieve his cosh or force his way out. George picked up the cosh from the carpet, regarded it thoughtfully and put it on the table with the collection of stolen goods.

For the next half-hour George questioned Pellicio closely. At first the answers came reluctantly, but two more Armagnacs and the affability of his captor loosened his tongue. George learned that the little Corsican had been a student at the Sorbonne in Paris and then had gone on the stage as an 'underman' in a troupe of acrobats, travelling through the countries of Europe. When the troupe dissolved because of an accident to one of the members, he took a job as footman with the Mayor of Rome and then became butler-valet to a well-known French nobleman to whom his knowledge of foreign capitals and European travel systems was of great value. He lost this position when his master discovered that he showed more interest in the contents of his safe than in valeting him.

'Why did he not hand you over to the police?' asked George.

Pellicio shrugged. 'I had a bundle of letters,' he answered, 'which he did not want disclosed.'

'What kind of letters?'

'Pure dynamite, Monsieur,' laughed Pellicio. 'I could have got ten thousand francs for them from the editor of the *Whip*.' He nodded sadly. 'I knew him very well, we were fellow students at the Sorbonne.'

'But you did not sell them? You kept them?'

'As a kind of insurance . . . I hope you will understand?'

'I understand perfectly,' answered George dryly. 'You need not explain any more. So the letters kept you out of prison.'

'But the master did not give me a reference after our little argument.'

'Quite understandable,' nodded George. 'So you could not find another job.'

'Precisely.'

'Did you look for one?'

'Certainly . . . at the beginning. But then came the travelling season and people closed their houses in Paris and went to live in indifferent hotels with bad service.' He looked around the room with disapproving eyes.

George laughed. 'You do not approve of hotels and hotel service?'

'No. Too sloppy and too impersonal.'

'And a bit too dangerous for any kind of side-line such as yours. I see your point clearly enough,' George continued. 'A talented young man like you must be independent and have a background which gives him all the opportunities he wants. Would you accept a job, if it were offered you?'

'Who would be foolish enough to employ me without any references?'

'Maybe I would,' said George.

'*You?*' cried Pellicio. 'You are pulling my leg. I was wondering the whole time why you asked me all the questions, and why I was such an imbecile to answer them. Now you are poking fun at me!'

'Not at all, my friend,' was the answer. 'I need a valet.'

'Me? You want me as your valet, Monsieur? Either I am completely crazy, or . . . or . . .'

'. . . or I am! That's what you wanted to say. Well perhaps I am.'

'Your valet!' said Pellicio, calmer now. 'After what I have told you. What are you up to, Monsieur? Do you want to reform me?'

'No,' answered George seriously. 'I do not want to reform you. If you have been a valet for three years with your previous master you must be quite good . . . *as a valet.* I believe that being my valet would appeal to your talent. Unless you prefer to continue pilfering from sleeping guests in badly-appointed hotel rooms. It is up to you. I have made my offer. You can take it or leave it. If you do not want it, you are free to go.'

The little burglar was visibly shocked. 'You mean I can just walk out . . .?'

'Exactly. Nobody is holding you.'

'I must be dreaming,' said Pellicio after a while. 'Who *are* you?'

'Quite a proper question,' said George. 'Didn't you know? My name is Prince Lahovary,' he added flippantly with a small bow.

'You are Prince Lahovary . . . ? I have heard of you. They say you are so rich you don't know what to do with your money.'

'Who told you that?'

'Below-stairs, Monsieur. Gossip in the servants' quarters. You tip like a prince.'

George smiled. 'So that's what they say about me?'

'But I still do not understand,' Pellicio went on. 'What use would I be to Prince Lahovary? Aren't you afraid that I would rob you the first day in your service?'

'That,' said George thoughtfully, 'is a risk I am prepared to take. It should be a very interesting experience. Anyway,' and he pointed to the small table, 'you have already tried and seen what comes of it. No. I do not believe that you would try again. I think you would be a very enthusiastic and loyal servant.'

'But what interest has Prince Lahovary in a small-time crook like me?'

'You are much too modest, my friend,' was the amicable reply. 'I like you and am offering you a job, so do not argue yourself out of an opportunity. I want someone to help me, and I believe that you are the right person.'

'Help you?' cried Pellicio. 'What help can I give you? What help do you want? Someone who puts your evening clothes on the bed? I can do that without any danger to your pearl studs. Or what else have you in mind . . . ? Do you want me to steal for you?'

'Exactly!'

Pellicio was speechless for a long time. 'You are not Prince Lahovary,' he said finally. 'Who are you?'

'Since you ask me a straight question, I will give you a straight answer. I am George Manolesco.'

At this revelation Pellicio jumped out of his chair, took Manolesco's hand and shook it. 'Manolesco!' he cried. 'My God, you *are* Manolesco? The Great Manolesco?! Do they not call you the Prince of Thieves? Now, everything is clear to me, Monsieur, and I will gladly link up with you. I am entirely at your service. What do you want me to do? Name it and I'll do it. The Great Manolesco! I still cannot believe it. This must be my lucky day, after all. Excuse me, Monsieur, but this calls for another drink!'

*   *   *

It never crossed George's mind that the little Corsican might have second thoughts and betray him. Any *commissaire de police* in any *préfecture* anywhere in France would have gladly paid 1,000 francs reward to catch Manolesco. He relied entirely on his judgement of men, which rarely let him down.

Pellicio left at 6 a.m. by way of the service stairs, leaving the booty with his new master. 'They might be suspicious when I walk out through the back entrance so early in the morning,' he explained. 'Seeing bulging pockets, they might even search me.'

They had agreed that George would take everything to Marseilles in his luggage, where they would meet late that evening. He gave Pellicio the money for the ticket and meals, then dressed and had breakfast in his room. He closed and locked his trunks and went down to the cashier's desk to pay his bill.

He reached the station of the Sud de la France railway with three minutes to spare before the departure of the morning express to Marseilles, and settled down in a reserved compartment. There had not been any message from the lady of the previous night, and he doubted very much that he would ever hear of her again.

He arrived at Marseilles's Nouvelle Gare du Sud at four in the afternoon, handed his luggage to the *huissier* from the Grand Hotel for transportation in the hotel omnibus and hired a carriage from the rank in front of the station. He dismissed the coachman in the Place Centrale at the fringe of the Old Town and walked along the rue Colbert into the rabbit-warren of small alleys between the Port and the Gare Centrale.

Carcola, now the biggest 'fence' of the century, received George, the biggest crook of the century, like a lost son and all his chins wobbled with pleasure as he embraced him and led him into his private office.

He agreed to pay 10,000 francs for the necklace. 'Not a centime more,' he added when George seemed not very enthusiastic at the offer.

'It is worth at least fifty thousand,' protested George. 'And there is not the slightest risk of anybody claiming it. It will be hushed up . . . as usual.'

Carcola shook his head in surprise. 'How the hell do you do it, George?' he asked. 'But honestly I cannot afford to pay more than ten. The market is not too good lately. I tell you what I'll do. I'll buy you a wonderful dinner at Girondy . . . bouillabaisse, mon ami, and what a bouillabaisse!'

'All right,' laughed George. 'The bouillabaisse does it, you old crook. Come on, let's go.'

Ten thousand-franc notes in his pocket, George left Carcola after a four-hour dinner and strolled slowly along the winding streets to the Maritime Station and his appointment with Pellicio. Pellicio stood in the booking hall, holding a small suitcase. It was a completely changed Pellicio. Dressed in a neat blue jacket, with discreetly striped, unwrinkled trousers, a white shirt and collar, a black tie and black hat, he was the image of the 'gentleman's gentleman'. When he saw his new master entering the station, he lifted his hat.

'Very well done,' was George's comment as they stepped out into the Place d'Arenc to take a carriage to the hotel on the Cannebière where George had reserved a first-floor suite overlooking the port. He signed the register as 'Prince Lahovary and valet'.

The Grand Hotel was the latest of the hotel-wonders of the end of the nineteenth century. It stood on the corner of the Cannebière Prolongée and the Allée Meilhan, the last word in comfort and luxury. It had 200 suites, all with electric light, and a hydraulic lift. Even Pellicio was impressed, especially by the elegant, bejewelled crowd of society ladies with their escorts in top hats and opera capes, arriving in landaus, hansom cabs and victorias at the rate of one a minute to be ushered into the gigantic Winter Garden hall for an after-theatre dinner.

They stayed three days in Marseilles, mostly in their rooms where they had long conferences. George put it very neatly many years later during his interrogation by his solicitor in Berlin: 'If two dogs meet one another, each knows that the other is a dog. We did not know each other. So we used the time to sniff around like two dogs and get better acquainted. We trusted one another about fifty per cent, which is a lot but not enough for a well-run partnership. Pellicio was a very careful, suspicious character, but so was I.'

However, they finally reached agreement on how the partnership should operate. George was to be the undisputed boss, Pellicio would receive a fixed salary plus a quarter of all future profits from their combined undertakings. While the two talked, George sat at the window of their sitting-room, practising old and new card-tricks. To see him handling the cards was a revelation to the Corsican. Sometimes George invited Pellicio to join him in a game of vingt-et-un or poker, and always ended up the winner. Pellicio, who had seen plenty of cheating at cards and who was frankly pre-warned by George, could never catch him.

'Do people not get suspicious of your luck?' Pellicio wanted to know.

George shook his head. 'No,' he answered. 'I never force the issue unnecessarily. Only if the need arrives. It would be a severe blow if it were discovered that Prince Lahovary cheated at cards. If I won too much, people would get suspicious. So I have to know precisely where and when to stop winning and to start losing. If you know what your partner will do you are always on the safe side with cards. It is roulette that is difficult. It always takes my money. And I have not yet found a way to correct the little machine.'

'You should have gone on the stage,' said Pellicio. 'As a magician you would have been a great success. You are throwing away a fortune.'

George enjoyed the tribute. 'It is not the first fortune I have thrown away,' he replied, 'and I suppose it will not be the last. There are about one thousand ways to cheat at cards, and I only know nine hundred, which is not at all satisfactory.'

George was then twenty-six years old.

Chapter 7

During the late spring of 1897, Prince Lahovary and his valet arrived in Baden Baden. There, during a poker session in the Hotel Cour de Bade that lasted almost without break for two nights and two days, George emptied the bulging wallets of two American visitors.

Pellicio turned out to be not only an excellent valet, but a most entertaining travelling companion with a deep knowledge of French art and literature that surprised his master, whose education in such subjects was very definitely lacking. In his luggage Pellicio always carried a couple of books of such eminent authors as Emile Zola and Victor Hugo, and often a French translation of a novel by Charles Dickens. In addition, the valet's knowledge of French society, the result of three years' service in Paris, was invaluable. It was due to Pellicio's intelligence reports that they departed for Vienna.

The valet's information had come from the servants' quarters of the Hotel Stephanie in Baden Baden where, as in all great international hotels, valets and personal maids discussed their masters and mistresses, their plans and habits, their wealth, sins and idiosyncrasies. Pellicio's news was of a Brazilian coffee planter, on a trip through Europe, who had departed for the Hotel Sacher in Vienna.

'He has so much money that it is easier for him to count his coffee-beans than his banknotes,' explained Pellicio. 'And, what is more, he is an enthusiastic gambler, losses do not worry him.'

So Prince Lahovary and valet booked in at the famous

hotel in Vienna. In the evening George went down to the terrace for supper.

'The Gaucho will be there,' said Pellicio. 'I will wait for Your Highness in the suite.'

The 'Gaucho', a tall, tanned man, was sitting at a small table and was the only other guest in the restaurant without a beautiful female companion.

Finally, George beckoned the *maître d'hôtel*. 'Tell me, Charles,' he said, 'who is the single gentleman over there?'

The *maître d'hôtel*, a great diplomat and the confidant of the politicians, archdukes, counts, princes and millionaires who populated the hotel, smiled discreetly. 'This is really amusing, Your Highness,' he answered with the friendly air of the great Viennese waiter; 'he asked me the same question about Your Highness five minutes ago.'

'Did he?' said George laughing. 'Did you tell him?'

'Certainly, Your Highness. I told him.'

'Any reason why he asked?'

'The usual reason—he thought he had met you before.'

'And what does he want?'

'I think he does not know many people in our city. He does not speak German or French. Only Brazilian and English.'

'An oversight in his education,' said George.

The *maître d'hôtel* suppressed a smile. 'He did not even bring his own valet,' he said disapprovingly, 'but has hired one for the length of his stay. It's the new way that they are doing things on the other side of the ocean.' With a faint note of disgust in his voice he added: 'I understand he is extremely wealthy. Coffee, I was told.'

'Charles,' laughed George. 'You are an incorrigible snob! What's wrong with coffee? Perhaps he has come to your fair city to buy himself an archduchess; it has been done before, you know.'

'Unfortunately so,' was the disgusted answer.

'However,' continued George, sliding a folded banknote towards the *maître d'hôtel*, 'ask the gentleman from the Pampas whether he would do me the honour of joining me for a brandy in the smoking room.'

Señor Caladenez was glad to make the acquaintance of

Prince Lahovary and they got on very well together. They went to a variety show at the 'Ronacher', then to the Prater Park for a midnight snack, and ended in a Czigan wine cellar in the early hours of the morning for chicken broth and gipsy music.

At 4 a.m. George suggested a visit to his club for a little game to complete a perfect day, and the Brazilian agreed eagerly. By six o'clock 15,000 kroner had changed owners after a friendly game of baccara.

Back in his suite George found Pellicio looking pleased and mysterious; from the pocket of his jacket he produced a beautiful platinum ring with a huge diamond.

George stared at the glittering jewel. 'Where did you get this?' he asked brusquely.

'Next door,' answered the little Corsican complacently. 'From an old woman there. She has a box full of them. A Baroness Hochstein, I think.'

'You bloody fool!' exploded George. 'You damned idiot! How often have I told you to keep your hands off anything in a hotel where we are staying. Get rid of it, and quickly!'

'But, Highness,' pleaded Pellicio, 'it's such a wonderful rock, and the door was open. I could never have missed the opportunity, I would have cursed myself.'

'You will have plenty of opportunity to curse yourself if they find the ring in your possession! Baroness Hochstein is the sister-in-law of the Minister of the Interior, who, as you perhaps know, runs the very efficient Viennese police. Her brother has married the daughter of Prince Radetzki, and one of her sons is the second aide-de-camp to the Emperor. She has enough connections to force the authorities to search even this hotel, with all its highly-placed guests. What is worse, she is thoroughly capable of doing it. Get rid of it, take it back if you want to; or throw it into the Danube!'

'But nobody has seen me, Highness.'

'I hope not,' said George grimly. 'Where was the maid?'

Pellicio had already recovered from his first shock. He grinned. 'When the old lady left, she ran down the corridor and right into the arms of the groom of the Archduke in room Number 209. Love is a wonderful thing, Highness.'

George stretched out his hand. 'Give me the ring, I'll handle this. If everything goes smoothly we will be leaving in the afternoon, and will spend a few days in Budapest. If not . . . well, we will spend the next months here. . . . Did you damage any locks in the room?'

'No. The door was open and the ring was on the table.'

'All right,' nodded George. 'Go back to your room now . . . and remember, never again be such a fool!'

When Pellicio had left, George went to the escritoire in the corner of his room, took a sheet of hotel notepaper and wrote a few words on it. Then he addressed an envelope to the Baroness Hochstein, wrapped the ring in another sheet of paper and put it with the note into the envelope and sealed it. Then he went down to the hall porter and gave him the letter for delivery. It was nearly 8 a.m. when he went to bed, still rather worried.

*   *   *

A knock at his door woke him at noon. A pass-key was inserted into the lock, the door opened and a page boy with a silver salver entered. On it was a letter.

It was from the Baroness Hochstein.

'The ring you found,' she wrote, '*is* mine. I am most grateful to you for returning it to me so quickly; would you join me for lunch in my private dining-room at 2 p.m., so that I can thank you personally?'

George took one of his crown-embossed visiting cards and wrote a short acceptance. Armed with a bunch of roses, he entered the Baroness's suite at two o'clock.

Baroness Hochstein had been one of the most celebrated Viennese hostesses. Very rich, very eccentric, and sometimes even charming, she was loved by the public for her outspoken comments on the idlers that thronged the Emperor's Court. Her biting remarks appealed to the Viennese and were quoted in every night club and cabaret in the city. Her distinguished victims feared her dangerous tongue.

A little, bird-like old lady with flaming red-dyed hair, and covered with jewels, she tripped towards George with outstretched hand.

'Mon cher Prince!' she cried in a high, piercing voice.
She was very fond of mixing French into her conversation.
'I am always so careless with my jewels. It was lucky you
found the ring and no one else.'

'I saw it lying in front of your door and I guessed it would
be yours.'

After lunch they went out on to the balcony for coffee.

'Lahovary?' suddenly said the Baroness, scrutinizing him
through her lorgnette. 'I knew a Prince Lahovary, but he is
an elderly man. Any relation of yours? It's a Romanian name,
isn't it?'

George knew very well whom his hostess had in mind, and
merely nodded for the moment. He always tried to stick as
close to the truth as possible, which made his status as
Prince Lahovary more credible.

'Yes,' he answered eventually. 'The poor relations,
Baroness! They live near Craiova, while we have our estate
in Ploesti. Oil, you know. It was discovered twenty years
ago. And of all places, where do you think? Directly in front
of the ballroom. It splashed all over the windows and the
walls. What a horrible mess! What dirt!'

'Dégoutant!' laughed the Baroness. 'But what a lot of
money!' she added impishly and sipped at her Chartreuse.

George chuckled. The Baroness was a woman after his
own heart, he like people who called a spade a spade.

'Certainly,' he agreed, 'but still, that is no consolation.'
And with a catch in his voice, he added: 'Money is *not* everything. Sometimes during the night I wake from my sleep and
see our beautiful mansion with the rambler roses in bloom—
you know, Grandmother planted them herself—now rotten,
smelling, derelict. My heart beats in agony.'

'Mon ami,' said the Baroness, 'you Balkan people are
much too sentimental. Besides, I am sure you have compensated yourself for the loss.'

'We built a new house at the other end of the town,' he
answered. 'If that is what you mean?'

It appeared that the Baroness was related to half the
aristocracy of Europe, and many of the names she mentioned
were well known to George. Of half a dozen he knew enough

details to suggest he was or had been on quite intimate terms with them. Which in a sense was true, for they were some of his best victims.

'But then, I am sure,' cried the old lady happily, 'that you must also know Valeria. Her husband is now the French Ambassador in Rome. They have been everywhere, here in Vienna, in Sofia, in Pera, in Madrid.'

'Do you mean Valeria de Boulogne?' he asked, perhaps a bit too quickly.

The Baroness looked at him quizzically. 'A charming woman, isn't she? Do you know her well? I was surprised that Valeria never mentioned it to me. Usually she tells me everything . . . including her men-troubles—of which she usually has plenty.'

'Does she?' said George coldly.

Baroness Hochstein laughed aloud in delight. 'Does that shock you, mon cher Prince? She certainly has. Or would you know? What with a husband twenty years older than she is. . . . Mind you, Maurice is a charming man, but so terribly busy with affairs of state. I must remember to tell Valeria about you when I see her next.'

'You must,' answered George. 'She might even remember me, although it was a very long time ago that we met.'

'She will certainly remember. She always does. Do you want me to convey a message to her?'

'Thank you very much, Baroness,' he answered politely, 'just tell her if you must that you have met George. I am quite sure she will be interested.'

Baroness Hochstein folded her lorgnette with a click and dropped it into her lap. She smiled conspiratorily.

'I quite understand,' she said cynically. 'So it was George? Simply George! I do appreciate your discretion, Prince Lahovary, and I am very glad to have made your acquaintance. I know I am a meddling old woman,' she smiled. 'It was a great pleasure to have chatted with you, one meets so very few gentlemen nowadays. You may rest assured your secret will be safe with me.'

* * *

Via Budapest, George and Pellicio returned penniless to the Riviera, but departed for Paris in a few days with ample funds for the immediate future. They took rooms at the Hotel Westminster on the rue de la Paix.

Soon, money was short again. One evening George was sitting on the terrace of the Café de la Paix watching the strollers along the brilliantly-lit boulevard. Tomorrow the hotel bill was due. Well, that was nothing to worry about, but there was the upkeep of his newly-bought carriage, the wages of the footman, coachman and groom and of Pellicio. All the rich had left the city for the south and George could think of no immediate way out of his difficulty. His sombre meditations were interrupted by a hand stretched across the small table. George did not even look up. It was one of the many *clochards*, the ragged beggars who slept under the Seine bridges and invaded the boulevards when the theatres emptied. They never spoke a word. The hand thrust under people's noses said plainly enough: GIVE!

George was automatically fumbling in his pocket for a small coin when he noticed something very peculiar about the outstretched hand. 'This,' he said to himself, 'is not the hand of a *clochard*.' Although it was not clean, it was long-fingered and expressive, with signs of careful grooming in the past. George was curious. He gave the man a coin and waited till he had made the round of the terrace before starting to follow him along the boulevard. Near the Madeleine he caught up with him and led him to a bench in the square, where both sat down.

The beggar, a youngish man, at first seemed frightened, but with a piece of silver George convinced him that he was not a spy from the *préfecture de police*, but a benevolent nobleman who might help him.

When he did come out with it, the beggar's tale was a strange one. His name was Vladimir and he had been employed as a private secretary by a Russian Grand Duke of great wealth. Every year they visited the Grand Duke's villa on the French Riviera, and during their stay there about eight months ago it was discovered that Vladimir was in love with his master's only daughter Feodora, and—worse—

that Feodora was in love with him. Now Vladimir had been born on one of the Grand Duke's own estates where serfdom still prevailed. When the Grand Duchess had taken an interest in him, he was sent to schools in Kiev and Moscow and trained as a secretary. Though an Imperial decree from the Court had officially banned serfdom, the laws of St. Petersburg had no meaning on the distant estates. The feudal landowners still had power over life and death. Vladimir had committed the deadly sin of wooing his master's daughter, a niece of the mighty Tsar, and had planned to elope with her to freedom far from her despotic father. When the affair was discovered the Grand Duke ordered his Cossack body-guards to keep Vladimir under lock and key. Feodora, chaperoned by a female member of the Ducal household, was sent to Lausanne to one of the most inaccessible and exclusive Swiss *pensionate de jeunes filles*.

In France there was nothing the Grand Duke could do to Vladimir but keep him prisoner, and it was clear to the young man that he would be held prisoner until the family returned to Russia. He did not dare to contemplate what he might expect there. Then an unguarded moment gave him the chance to escape, penniless, to Paris.

'Now,' Vladimir said, 'I have heard that Feodora is in Paris. She is being forced by her father to marry a French nobleman and tomorrow a reception will be held to announce the engagement.'

When they parted long after midnight, George, genuinely touched by the story, asked Vladimir to meet him on the same bench in two night's time. 'Perhaps I may find a solution for your troubles.'

In the morning George started some hard thinking. He knew the Grand Duke in question and felt that it would be a pleasure to outwit him—apart from any money that might be knocking around. After a very early breakfast he took a stroll along the river that brought him to a bistro near Notre-Dame, in the Old Cité, one of the best places to tap the grape-vine of the underworld. Here he found two men he had met in prison, who grinned cheerfully when he sat down at their table.

'Pleased to see you again, George,' said one of them. 'We heard you were back in town. Yes, we'll have a Calvados, thank you. Things are not too good at the moment.'

'Are they not?' asked George. 'What is the trouble?'

'Too many *flics* around,' was the answer. 'You do not bother, we know; you work differently. But we are only poor crooks!'

'And what do you hear and see?'

'Odds and ends. There is not so much coming our way, George. But did you know that a person has come up from the south, as rich as they make them . . .? Might be up your street.' He swallowed the rest of his Calvados. 'Thanks, yes, I'll have another one,' he nodded. 'He is supposed to be a cousin or a nephew of the Russian Emperor.'

Grand Duke Alexander Alexandrovich *had* arrived! Apparently he had taken an entire floor at the Hôtel Vendôme, practically next door to the hotel in which George was registered.

One of the last two fifty-franc notes in George's possession passed across the table, and George made his way to the rue Castiglione, where he knew a little tobacco stand, 200 yards from the Hôtel Vendôme, whose crippled owner was friendly with most of the hotel employees in the district. For twenty francs the cripple provided the information that the Grand Duke had bought his daughter a diamond tiara, to be delivered at his hotel during the afternoon before the reception. Back at the Westminster, George had a session with Pellicio, and then ordered his carriage. It was now 11 a.m.

'I had an excellent, if early, *déjeuner*,' he recollected, 'during which I gave my deplorable financial status some thought.' Surely it would be best to find more money before he started out doing anything to help Vladimir. He told Pellicio to remain in the hotel until his return, went down to his carriage and rode away.

There were but a handful of jewellers in Paris where a man like Grand Duke Alexander would buy a diamond tiara. One was Fontana, but according to Pellicio the Russian aristocracy did most of their jewel-hunting at Cartier's in the rue de la Paix, not more than a few steps from his hotel. This suited George very well. He told the salesman that he wished to choose a small gift as a present for a young Russian lady who was getting engaged to a French nobleman.

The salesman smiled innocently. 'As a matter of fact,' he said, 'His Royal Highness, the Grand Duke Alexander Alexandrovich, has bought a tiara here for his daughter.'

That was just what George wanted to know. He ordered a small brooch for 900 francs and told the salesman to send it to the hotel after four in the afternoon. 'The hall porter will pay you,' he said, adding silently: 'I hope . . .' and while the salesman wrote down the instructions, he slipped into his pocket a diamond ring and a small golden cross with aquamarines and diamonds. It was most unlikely that the jewellers would accuse H.H. Prince Lahovary of theft when they discovered that the two trinkets were missing. A guest at the Grand Duke's reception who had given an address at one of the premier hotels of the city could not be suspect.

He dismissed his carriage at the Bastille, walked to Machinelle's little office, and found the 'fence' just about to leave for the ever-important lunch hour. After some haggling he got 2,500 francs for the two pieces of jewellery which were worth 8,000 francs on an honest market. He hurried back to his hotel and gave the hall porter 1,000 francs to pay Cartier's messenger. With his credit at the hotel maintained, he went to his suite, had a bath and called in Signor Marione, the barber. A short conference with Pellicio followed, and when at four a page boy finally brought the small parcel from the jewellers, he took his cane and top hat and walked placidly to the hotel on the other side of the Place Vendôme.

The hotel foyer was crowded with guests. At the entrance to the ballroom two footmen announced each guest. On a big table in the corner of the ballroom were exhibited the hundreds of gifts to the young couple.

George was loudly announced: 'His Highness Prince Lahovary,' and at the foot of the entrance steps he was met by the Grand Duke himself, a tall, handsome man of military bearing, with a small pointed beard, and a hard smile on his lips. George had met the Grand Duke in a gambling club in Cannes, and had even played with him, luckily for his present purpose, without cheating.

'My dear Prince Lahovary,' said the Grand Duke. 'This is a special honour. Come, let me present you to my daughter, Feodora.'

The girl was pale and ill-at-ease. She shook hands with George, accepting with a nod the parcel George had brought, and passed it unopened to a footman who carried it over to the table to join the rest of the presents. Beside Feodora stood a middle-aged Frenchman, a Baron de Carosse, whom the Duke introduced as the groom-to-be. Even if he had not been prejudiced against him beforehand, George did not like the man, a self-important, bombastic fellow. George had never heard the name Carosse, and guessed correctly that he was one of the thousands of former courtiers of the defunct French Imperial Court. He was at least twenty years older than the beautiful Russian girl whose sad eyes betrayed her unhappiness. Why a man in the position of the Grand Duke had picked such a specimen of mediocrity for a son-in-law, George could not fathom; perhaps it was but to punish his daughter and spite Vladimir.

George sauntered from guest to guest, admired the gifts, and stared with interest at the detectives from the *préfecture* posted at each corner of the table. With them were two men of a stature George had never seen before, obviously the Cossack bodyguards. On a black velvet cushion in the centre of the table lay the glittering diamond tiara. There were at least two million francs in jewels here . . . but they could not be stolen!

George walked out of the ballroom, collected his hat and cane, but instead of leaving the hotel, he went up the stairs to the first floor, where the Grand Duke had his suite. He walked quietly along the empty corridors, and tried the doors of several rooms. They were locked.

At last he came to one that was ajar. He knocked and when there was no answer, entered. It proved to be the drawing-room of the Grand Duke's suite. George closed the door and went to the window, where he pulled back the curtains for more light. Left and right the doors to the next rooms were open. One room was a lady's *salon* in the Louis XIV style, the other, small and narrow, was used as a writing-room.

Obviously the Grand Duke would not leave the presents in the ballroom. This particular suite George knew only too well from a visit a few years ago, when he had found in the drawing-room a wall safe built in behind a fine reproduction of the old Italian school. (These safes had no combination locks and opened with a simple handle.) He prepared for a long wait. From the small writing-room he carried a chair to the space between the tall windows of the drawing-room, placed it behind the heavy curtains, which he now pulled to, and sat down cross-legged on the chair to avoid his shoes being seen from the room. He sat there unmoving, top hat firmly on his head, cane hung over the chair arm.

Five hours later, after midnight, the doors of the drawing-room were thrown open and the Grand Duke and his daughter entered, preceded by a maid and a footman carrying lights, and followed by a cavalcade of hotel employees with trays, boxes and parcels containing the presents. The giant Cossacks brought up the rear. The servants put their burdens on the table in the centre, bowed and departed. A footman had in the meantime lit small side-chandeliers, then the doors were closed. There were now in the room, the Grand Duke, his daughter, the two Cossacks—and George peering between the curtains.

On a sign from their master, the Cossacks removed the Italian picture from the wall and opened the safe. Within a few moments, the boxes and parcels were placed inside, the door was closed and the picture restored to its original position. Then the Cossacks posted themselves right and left of the picture. During the whole time not a word was spoken by the young Duchess Feodora. She stood listlessly near the door. George had no doubt that her heart was elsewhere, longing for Vladimir and dreading the future.

Finally everything seemed to be arranged to the satisfaction of the Grand Duke and he led his daughter into the adjoining *salon*. The door was closed and the guards stood motionless by the picture. Now and then they exchanged a few words in Russian, which George did not understand. The great hotel and the street outside fell quite silent. The hours passed, until George could hear a distant bell striking 5 a.m. Then came the faint tap-tap of the municipal gas man, running along the street, putting out the lamps. Then once more came absolute silence.

George sat on. The clock struck the half-hour. Suddenly a loud voice came from the corridor. Someone rattled at the door. George smiled. The noise outside grew in volume. The two Cossacks said something excitedly, and when whoever it was started to hammer on the door, they both ran towards it, opened it, and rushed out. They could be heard pounding along the corridor in full pursuit of the noise-maker.

George went into action. He knew he had but a few minutes; he removed the picture from the wall, opened the safe and crammed as many of the presents as he could into the specially deep pockets of his frock-coat. He replaced the empty boxes, closed the safe, hung the picture, and calmly carried his chair back into the writing-room. As the noises from the corridor seemed to die down, he opened the window of the writing-room, pressed his top hat more firmly on his head, stepped over the small gilded balcony railing, and slid down the drain-pipe into the deserted rue Castiglione.

Within three minutes he had reached his hotel and went in through the back entrance with the first flood of employees of the day shift. In their own suite Pellicio looked at the tiara, which George estimated to be worth at least 400,000 francs.

'So, you performed your conjuring trick,' said Pellicio as George stretched out on the bed.

'Jean was excellent,' replied George. 'His disturbance was a first-class performance. It distracted all attention. I only hope they haven't beaten him up too much or even killed him. How did he get into the hotel?'

'He simply rushed in, acting very drunk and charged up to the Grand Duke's suite.'

'You are a good instructor, Pellicio,' said George. 'Now for a well-earned rest, and later we'll see what we can do for Jean.'

Within two hours an inspector of the police was announced and courteously received by George. He informed him that a man, arrested for causing a disturbance in the Hôtel Vendôme, had said that he was in the employ of Prince Lahovary. He had explained that he had mistaken the Vendôme hotel for that of the Prince.

George laughed. 'He had a night out and probably too much to drink.'

The inspector nodded understandingly. 'If His Highness would pay the fine the man could be released at once.'

Naturally Prince Lahovary paid the ridiculous sum of 100 fancs. Now he had to act swiftly if he did not want to land in serious trouble. Seemingly the theft of the jewels had not yet been discovered, otherwise the 'drunk' would have been detained. George sat down at the writing desk and composed an extraordinary and audacious letter. He wrote:

Dear Grand Duke Alexander Alexandrovich,

A strange tale has come to my knowledge that you were opposed to the marriage of your beautiful daughter to the man she loves, and that you are forcing her to become the wife of a French pauper, who could be her father.

I hate despotism and injustice, and most of all I hate people who try to break the hearts and the spirits of two youngsters in love.

Therefore I have taken it upon myself to secure justice.

During the night I relieved you of many of the valuable presents so strongly guarded in your drawing-room. You may be wealthy enough to afford the loss of some million francs' worth of jewels, but I doubt if you wish to be the laughing-stock of Paris, should I decide to make public the whole story. I can quite imagine that your relations in St. Petersburg would not appreciate a public scandal, and you would have a very chilly reception when returning to Russia.

Therefore I suggest that you give me a written undertaking to call off the proposed wedding and consent to your daughter marrying the man of her choice. I will return to you the valuables which found their way into my possession, with the exception of the wonderful tiara which you bought yourself. This I consider as my commission and your penalty for your attitude. Part of my proceeds will go to your future son-in-law as a gift from you. You will then, upon my word of honour, hear no more of the unfortunate affair.

Should you decline to do as I wish, you will never see any of the gems and I would find myself forced to tell the entire story to a friend of mine on that well-known paper *La Trompette*, with whom I have an appointment tonight for dinner.

I am, my dear Grand Duke Alexander Alexandrovich,
Yours sincerely,
George Manolesco.

Pellicio delivered the letter to the Hôtel Vendôme, and returned after one hour with the Grand Duke's answer. He agreed in full to George's demands.

'In Russia you never know what will happen,' commented George happily. 'To make the story public could have meant a journey to Siberia for our poor friend the Grand Duke.'

He sent back the gems (though reluctantly) and sold the tiara to Machinelle for a quarter of its value. Then he returned to his hotel, paid the bill and, while Pellicio packed the trunks, went to the Hôtel Vendôme. He sent up his PRINCE LAHOVARY card to the Grand Duke and scribbled on it: 'Recommended by our mutual friend George Manolesco.'

He was received at once, with deadly, icy politeness.

'Your Royal Highness,' said Manolesco, 'I came to seek your permission to make an appointment with your daughter for tonight.'

Without a word, the Grand Duke summoned Feodora. 'You may talk freely with this gentleman,' he said and marched out of the room.

George told Feodora some of the story but did not disclose the reason for the sudden change of mind of her illustrious papa. He collected a radiant girl in the evening and drove her to the Madeleine. There on the same bench as forty-eight hours ago sat Vladimir, waiting but probably expecting nothing.

When the carriage stopped at the corner of the rue Royale, Feodora saw the hunched figure on the bench. In a second she was out of the carriage door and had flown into the arms of her beloved. For minutes they forgot George waiting smilingly in the carriage, until he went over to them and pressed a bundle of banknotes into Vladimir's hand. 'Here,' he said, 'are your savings, returned by your future father-in-law. And a small present for your engagement.' It was 10,000 francs. He turned on his heels and went back to his carriage. 'To the hotel, Jean,' he ordered.

Only when the carriage was moving rapidly away did Vladimir recover enough to shout: 'Monsieur! Monsieur!' But the carriage had already disappeared in the direction of the Opéra.

The trunks were packed and Pellicio waiting. They drove to the Gare du Nord for the night train to Frankfurt. George thought it wiser to leave France for a while, one never knew what pull such exalted people as the Grand Duke might have. When all their luggage was stored away on the train, George addressed his groom. 'Jean,' he said, 'here is one thousand francs for your services, and to thank you for your excellent performance last night, you may keep the carriage and the horses.'

It was in the great Hotel Frankfurter Hof a few weeks later that George picked up a Paris newspaper. In the gossip column was a paragraph saying that Feodora's engagement to her French nobleman was broken off and that instead she would marry her childhood love, Vladimir. The Grand Duke had kept his word.

Years afterwards George met Vladimir again. He had become a naturalized Frenchman and, thanks to his knowledge of the Slav languages, held a good position in one of the big new tourist offices that had become so popular with the growing travelling public. Feodora was as beautiful as George remembered her. She and Vladimir were happy and still much in love. The Grand Duke visited them regularly every year, watching a little Feodora growing up as the image of her mother.

Chapter 8

Prince Lahovary and his valet stayed four weeks at Frankfurt on Main, occupying a four-roomed suite on the second floor of the Frankfurter Hof. They were the richer from several successful gambling sessions with a party of Latin-American businessmen, and now their trunks were packed and ready to be carried to the station for the afternoon express to Lucerne in Switzerland, where George usually spent a few weeks of the summer season. Neither George nor Pellicio had taken a great liking to Frankfurt—the people were too careful and parsimonious gamblers, while the women were much too occupied with homes and children to bother overmuch about appearance, much less jewels.

'Home-made cakes,' snorted George. More bluntly Pellicio averred that all German women were cows, and consorted with the personal maid of an Italian opera singer he had met in the servants' hall. But, to his utter disgust, after ten days of romance she fell for a bull-necked, heel-clicking Prussian batman to a German army officer. Pellicio next consoled himself with a fat yodeller from Bavaria. All the time the valet kept criticizing the hotel service. He started counting the chipped cups and saucers.

'So far,' he informed George one morning, 'we have had twenty-one third-rate pieces of crockery to eat from. God knows the cups are thick enough to be thrown against a wall without danger of breaking. How they do it is a riddle to me, but anyway, this place is lacking in standing.'

George laughed. 'You are a snob, Pellicio,' he said. 'If you had your way, I believe you would force me to have my suspenders ironed every day, or to wear a top hat to bed.'

'This is no laughing matter,' answered Pellicio. 'You are Prince Lahovary, and let me tell you that it is unworthy of you to endure such sloppy treatment.'

'All right,' nodded George. 'What's your remedy?'

'Quite simple,' said Pellicio. 'Get yourself your own breakfast utensils. Silver sugar bowl, silver marmalade pot, knives, forks, spoons, and some really good thin cups, saucers and plates!'

'And?'

'Have them engraved with your crown and initials and send them down to the kitchen to be used for the morning meal. . . .'

If Pellicio was a snob, George certainly was a greater one. The idea appealed to him but he had no intention of going to a jeweller's shop and paying good money for a set of silver dishes. He said so to Pellicio.

'Exactly,' nodded the valet. 'I never thought for a moment you would be so foolish as to buy the stuff. There are other ways.'

'Steal them?' asked George. 'You are crazy! I am not carrying around a load of silver hidden under my coat. That is out.'

'No one suggests it,' answered Pellicio with dignity. 'We can get all we want from a friend of mine—for next to nothing.'

It was thus that George met Ignaz Skamperl, a Hungarian music-hall artist, whose name Pellicio had discovered on the bill of the 'Coffeehouse-Variety Orpheum', where he was advertised as:

PRINCE NICOTIN

THE ONE AND ONLY MAN
who smokes 100 cigarettes
in 10 minutes
on the open stage
without
the help of machinery
or
hidden gadgets.

THE SENSATION OF PARIS, ROME, LONDON AND BERLIN
For the first time in Frankfurt

Pellicio had been with the 'Prince' on the same bill at the Alhambra in Copenhagen, when he was a variety artist.

'Ignaz has many good connections in the right circles,' explained Pellicio. 'He will be able to supply what you want, and besides, he might come in useful one day. He is very friendly with the Christiansens of Christiana.'

The Christiansens in Norway were famous as diamond 'fences'. They were four brothers, two of them cat burglars travelling regularly across Europe, the others running a small jeweller's shop in Christiana from which they disposed of stolen goods. George had heard of them and admired their brilliant team-work.

'Prince Nicotin', a tall, lean man with a jaundiced complexion and nervous, jerky movements, was pleased to meet the great Manolesco. For only 500 marks he promised a set of first-class breakfast silver to specifications supplied by George. 'No monograms to erase,' emphasized Pellicio.

'I think I know where I can get hold of it——' their new friend began, but George cut him short. 'I am not interested in where you get it,' he said haughtily, 'but only that you get it.'

'You will have the entire set the day after tomorrow,' was the answer.

Two days later Pellicio went to the Pension Vorster, a small boarding-house in the Lindenstrasse, to collect the silver from Skamperl. George valued the set at about 3,000 marks. 'I also went to Stetzelmann, the cigar shop near the station,' explained Pellicio, 'and bought five thousand cigarettes, which I gave Skamperl as a special gift with your compliments. You know, he is a heavy smoker.'

That evening the two went to see the performance at the Orpheum in the Zeil where 'Prince Nicotin' smoked his 100 cigarettes in ten minutes to the cheers of the nearly all-male audience. George, however, was far more interested in a dancer with a breathtaking figure. Introduced to her by 'Nicotin', he took her to the exclusive restaurant, Prinz von Arkadien. A casual hour or two in her room, and George arrived back at his hotel in the small hours of the morning.

They were to leave that day, but there was no sign of Pellicio. He turned up when George had already taken his bath and was sitting down to breakfast. Pellicio was smiling, mockingly.

'I thought they'd got you,' said George, 'and I think it would have served you right. Now you have had your way. We bought the breakfast silver. Where is it? I am still enduring chipped cups and saucers. What have you to say?'

'Only this,' said Pellicio, putting his hand in his pocket and producing a diamond bracelet. George examined it carefully. 'How did you get this?' he asked slowly.

'It was *given* to me,' said Pellicio.

'Given to you?' sneered George, gazing again at the bracelet. 'Who the hell gives *you* diamonds worth ten thousand francs?'

'A lady,' answered Pellicio smiling.

'Will you please explain clearly? You did not get it in the hotel, I hope?'

'Not at all,' said Pellicio. 'In a private house. I have forgotten to tell you about Lucille—I met her a few days ago in the Palmgarten during the concert. She is French and a very nice girl. She is the maid of a Frankfurt lady, and yesterday she invited me for a coffee and a glass of brandy to her room. You will agree, George, I could not very well refuse such a kind invitation. Her lady was out, but returned at about two o'clock in the morning and rang for Lucille. What a cheek! The poor girl had to dress in a hurry and I was left alone. So I decided to dress as well and have a little look around while Lucille was occupied. When I came to Madame's boudoir and peered through the door, she was standing there, half undressed—by the way a very nice figure—and on the dressing-table was that bracelet.

'At about three Lucille came out. She did not see me hiding behind a bookcase in the corridor and must have thought that I had left. So after a while I opened the door of the boudoir and entered. Madame was still sitting in front of the mirror and thought it was Lucille entering.

' "Qu'est-ce-qu'il-y-a?" she asked, and I wished her a polite "bonsoir, Madame".

'She turned round then and looked at me, surprised but not frightened. "What do you want?" she asked.

' "The diamonds, Madame, please," I said truthfully.

'She considered that for a few moments and then glanced at the bell near the door, but it was too far for her to reach. So she just took the bracelet and gave it to me. I said: "Thank you, Madame," bowed, and went to the door, and left the house by the front entrance.'

'And did she not ring, or raise the alarm?'

'No. I took the precaution to unscrew the electric bell at the door and to tear out the wire as an additional safety measure before I left.'

George considered the story. 'Well,' he said finally, 'does Lucille know who you are or where you live?'

'No. She thinks I am a commercial traveller.'

'Have you been followed?'

'No. I walked to the station, had a bath and then took a carriage to the hotel.'

'Not bad at all,' said George. 'Let's hope they do not pick on you. What do you want to do with it?'

'Skamperl,' said Pellicio. 'He can dispose of it! After all we can always use some money, especially after you have bought the silver!'

Pellicio returned to the hotel, 3,000 marks the richer, in time to supervise the loading of Prince Lahovary's luggage on the hotel omnibus. His Highness paid the bill and then took a carriage to the station to catch the express to Basle and Lucerne.

* * *

They were very old ladies, kind-hearted and unfashionably polite. They were dressed in a fashion some twenty years out-of-date, yet they did not look ridiculous. They lived near Lucerne and every afternoon they came to listen to the promenade concert, walking hand-in-hand, looking like two figures from a colour plate of bygone days. Regularly they settled down on the same bench to knit.

George had made their acquaintance three years earlier, as George Manolesco. They told him that they were two sisters who had married two brothers from Liechtenstein, but both husbands had died in a mountain accident. They were born in Braila in Romania, and were thrilled to find that George also was a Romanian and that they could talk to someone in their native language. When all three agreed that there was nothing better in the world than a Ploesti *chicken-pilav* baked in tomato sauce and Parmesan cheese, or a *tamaiosa*, or a *sarmali* rolled in bacon and served with sour cream, George was invited to their little cottage on the outskirts for a genuine home-cooked Romanian supper.

The next evening at eight he opened the little wooden gate and walked up the flagstoned path through the flower-filled garden. His hostesses had donned black lace gowns with white lace collars and cuffs, and long, sweeping trains. They wore no jewels, but their white hair above pink cheeks and smiling eyes gave them dignity.

They accepted the carnations George brought and led him through a tiny hall into a surprisingly large and pleasant drawing-room, with windows on three sides. It was crammed with chairs and small tables, knick-knacks, vases and standard lamps, and the walls were literally covered with pictures. Most of these were small and in silver frames. On a grand piano and on the mantelpiece were bowls of Alpine flowers, their sweet scent filling the room.

Amelia, the elder sister, came forward with a large bottle and glasses. 'It is elderberry wine,' she said. 'I hope you like it. We make it ourselves.'

Both sisters adjourned to the kitchen to finish preparing the meal and George, glass in hand, went round the room to look at the pictures. There were many family groups of large men with whiskers and beards, women with good-natured, peasant faces as large as their men-folk. One picture showed the wedding of the two sisters, and over the sideboard, larger than all the others, was an oil painting in a heavy gilt frame. A young man in a dark frock-coat and top hat held a silver-mounted walking-stick, and in his button-hole was a white gardenia. On his left hand could be seen a large diamond ring. He, too, had a fierce moustache and long side-whiskers. But his forehead was narrow and his

smile forced and false. It was not a nice face, and George did
not like it.

The meal—a perfect one—was taken on a little terrace.
The two old ladies were as happy as children, and when dusk
began to fall they settled in the drawing-room. Amelia lit the
lamps while Ileana drew the heavy velvet curtains. Although
George could be ruthless as a crook, he was at heart as
home-loving as anyone and now, for a few moments, he
loved the cottage and its contrast with the cold impersonality
of Europe's Grand Hotels.

A beam of light from one lamp now particularly illuminated
the painting of the young man. Ileana saw George glancing
at it and smiled. 'It is a nice picture, isn't it?' she asked.

George nodded. 'Who is it?'

'Why . . . it is Michael,' twittered Ileana. 'He is our
brother-in-law . . . or rather our step-brother-in-law. Our
father-in-law remarried when his wife died, and Michael is
the son of his second wife from a previous marriage. He is a
very nice boy, he manages our affairs. We do not understand
much about finances and with his help we can enjoy life
without any worries.

'I did not want to pry into your affairs,' said George
apologetically.

'That's quite all right,' said Ileana. 'As a matter of fact
we like to talk about Michael, because he really is such a
pillar of comfort to us. And he himself would never mention
the good things he has done for us.'

It appeared that Michael, a banker in Vienna, had been
appointed executor under the wills of both their husbands.

'You will have heard of Steinegger & Co?' said Ileana
proudly. 'Michael's name is Steinegger after his mother, and
not Wunderer, as ours. His bank keeps our accounts.'

For the next fortnight George met the two old ladies
every afternoon on the bench on the promenade, took them
on carriage drives, and then he invited them to a farewell
dinner at his hotel. From then on, every year when he visited
Lucerne, he enjoyed at least one Romanian supper at their
cottage.

Now, on the first day of their arrival, George left Pellicio in his suite at the Hotel National in the afternoon and went to the lake promenade to meet his friends at their usual bench. The bench was empty. He stayed through the two-hour concert, but the two old ladies did not appear. Nor did they come the next day. He went to the cottage to find a pleasant-looking Swiss woman who told him: 'We bought the cottage from them.'

That was odd. Both sisters had told him, so often, how happy they were in their little house and that they would never go away as long as they lived. 'What happened to them?' he asked.

'They just went away. I do not know where they have gone.'

Disappointed and upset, George went to the Town Hall to make inquiries, but without success. He asked the gardener in the park, but he did not know. He even went to the police, only to draw a blank. He returned to the hotel and ordered Pellicio to pack their trunks. He had come to see his old friends; there was no sense in staying longer. In six days he had an appointment with his solicitor in Vienna, and he decided to go to Zürich in the meantime: perhaps he could pass the time by picking up some worth-while lady visitor.

However, the two old ladies occupied his mind more than he ever thought possible. Their sudden disappearance and the sale of their beloved cottage worried him to such an extent that he nearly fumbled a job with the jewels of a South American lady he had met on the train from Lucerne.

'I know,' he told his valet, 'I will never be the old George again, unless I solve the mystery of Ileana and Amelia. If there *is* a mystery.'

Pellicio shook his head and advised George strongly not to let his personal feelings and emotions get the better of him. He told him of a striking Spanish dancer in a cabaret in the old town, but George for the first time in his life was not interested in amorous adventure. He went for long walks in the park along the lake or dozed in a deck-chair on the hotel terrace. On the day of their departure from Zürich he sent Pellicio to the travel office to get sleeping-car reservations. Then he went for a stroll along the Bahnhofstrasse. Suddenly someone touched his arm, and a small, excited voice cried: 'George! George Manolesco!' He turned round.

It was Ileana! Her pleasant face seemed a little smaller and her smile masked a worried expression. To the amusement of the passers-by they embraced, and George took Ileana's arm. At the bridge that crosses the Limmat, George signalled a carriage to take the excited old lady home. She protested that she could easily walk or take an omnibus, but in the end she gave in.

She lived in the Old Town under the Züriberg. In the basement was an Italian wine-shop with a noisy argument in full swing. Dozens of urchins played in the narrow street and at the corner a barrel-organ grinder poured out his music unceasingly. Through a dark hallway, she led George up a winding staircase to the top floor. She lived in two small rooms with ugly, heavy furniture and a worn carpet, but everything was spotlessly clean.

'Where is Amelia?' asked George, when he had taken the proffered chair.

'She died four months ago,' was the answer.

'Is that why you sold the cottage?'

She shook her head. 'No. We left together, about eight months ago. We could not afford it any longer.'

'That does not make sense,' said George. 'It was your own cottage, wasn't it?'

She nodded sadly and then told him what had happened. A year ago the usual quarterly draft from Vienna did not arrive. The two old ladies waited patiently but when after another three months no news came from Michael's bank and their ready cash started to run out, they decided to write to Vienna. 'Perhaps the money did not arrive by an oversight, and would dear Michael excuse their bothering him.'

They received an answer by return mail. Not a personal letter from Michael, as usual, but a cold business letter from the bank, telling them that there was nothing known of an allowance to be sent to the old ladies. Mr. Michael Steinegger had unfortunately died, and his widow, Madame Steinegger, now managed the bank. No accounts of the ladies could be traced in the bank's books. If the ladies had received any money, Madame was sure that her late husband had sent such money out of his own pocket.

It was a great shock, and they sent a second letter to the bank, saying that their entire fortune was deposited there. They did not even get a reply.

'Why did you not go and see a lawyer?' asked George.

'Heavens no!' she cried. 'How could we do such a thing? Michael had always been good to us. His sudden death must have been a great shock to his poor wife. Perhaps Michael had really helped us from the goodness of his heart, without telling anybody.'

George shook his head in despair at so much trust. As he listened to the rest of the story he had a sudden vision of the oil painting in the little cottage in Lucerne and the face he had disliked so strongly.

In the end the two old ladies had had to sell the cottage, and then Amelia became ill. Most of the money they received for the house went in medical treatment, but Amelia did not want to live any more. She simply died of a broken heart.

George explained that he was travelling to Vienna that night and would have a word with Madame Steinegger. Ileana gave him copies of the wills of their late husbands in which quite a sizeable fortune was mentioned as being in trust for them at the banking house of Steinegger & Co. 'I'll be back in about a week,' said George, when he kissed her good-bye. 'Perhaps I shall have news for you.'

Thanks to one of his Vienna associates, Herr Katz, who told him of the arrival in Vienna of a French jeweller as fond of gambling as of gems, good food, wine and women, George not only won 8,000 Swiss francs from the Frenchman, but the next night took his beautiful wife out to supper. He returned her to her hotel, safe and sound except for a sapphire-and-diamond necklace, which must have come unfastened in the carriage during a tender embrace. The next morning Pellicio was on his way to nearby Pressburg on the Danube, where the Slovak 'fence' paid a fair price. He returned to Vienna in the evening with a large bundle of banknotes. George also had a very good Press! The evening papers made quite a sensation of the missing necklace, and he found it advisable to change hotels. He took a small room in the commercial Hotel Kummer in the Mariahilferstrasse, and registered under the name of George Mercadente. Pellicio lodged privately with a Viennese family. Now it was time to tackle Madame Steinegger, and just in case, it was better to cover all traces.

George drove to the Spiegelgasse, where the banking house of Steinegger & Co. occupied a narrow-fronted Baroque building. Twelve marble steps led to the plate-glass swing doors. An imposing flunkey in red breeches and black coat lifted his top hat as he opened the door of George's carriage.

Producing his impressive visiting card, George asked to see Madame Steinegger. He was led through the hall to a room at the back. From behind a large ebony desk rose a lady; she was tall, blonde, superbly groomed and wearing a tailor-made costume in the latest fashion. She gave him her hand. 'I am Madame Steinegger,' she said in a husky voice. 'What can I do for you, Prince Lahovary?'

George looked around. The big top of the desk was completely bare except for a glass vase of yellow flowers. Behind Madame's high-backed chair hung two oil paintings—one of an old gentleman with a pleasant face, a top hat and a cane, and the other of Michael Steinegger. Apart from a visitor's chair there was no other furniture in the room. The walls were brocade-covered and on the highly-polished parquet floor was a steel-grey Smyrna carpet.

'I would like to know about the account of the ladies Wunderer,' said George.

'There is no such account,' said Madame swiftly. 'If, as they wrote, they received money from my husband, he must have sent it privately.' Her friendliness had vanished. 'He always had an open hand,' she added caustically.

'Quite so,' said George; 'but then there must be some entry in his private account?'

'Possibly,' agreed Madame. 'But when the bank was burgled about a year ago, the thieves took not only a large sum of money, but also some of the books.'

'Is that so?' said George slowly. 'But someone must remember such transfers, or even the name of Wunderer.'

Madame merely shrugged.

'Can I,' George continued, 'have a word with your head book-keeper?'

She stared for a second at him, then pressed an electric bell under the desk and a few moments later a young man entered.

'Herr Grandel, my head book-keeper,' said Madame. George shook hands and at once started to put his questions.

'No,' said Grandel with a glance at Madame, 'there are no records of money privately transferred, and I cannot remember such an entry in the private ledger of the late Mr. Steinegger.

'Thank you,' said George as he stood up. He bowed to Madame and went to the door. When he reached it, however, he turned round. 'By the way,' he said, 'have you been employed long with Steinegger & Co., Herr Grandel?'

It was Madame who answered the question. 'Several years,' she snapped. 'Why?'

'Pure curiosity,' smiled George. 'And thank you again!'

Madame looked at him now with open hostility, pushed her chair back and approached her visitor. Her voice was calm and icy. 'Sir!' she said. 'In view of your rude and incredible insinuations I should call the police. Would you please leave at once, and I will thank you never to come back.'

'Funny,' recalled George later, 'people always suggest that they should call the police, and then don't. I have ever thought that a sure sign that they have something to hide. It happened so often to me that I found it boring!'

He was now convinced that something queer was going on. He was certain that there must be, somewhere, *another* head book-keeper.

In a coffee-house he was introduced to a partner in a firm of bank auditors. 'Do you know the head book-keeper of Steinegger?' he asked the old man.

'Tinderer? Why, I have known him for more than thirty years.'

'That seems to be impossible,' said George. 'He is scarcely older than thirty. And his name is not Tinderer.'

The auditor laughed drily. 'You mean that young whipper-snapper Grandel. I am talking of the head book-keeper, who was with Steinegger for seventeen years. He's retired now.'

'Old age?' asked George.

'No, sir. He could not see eye to eye with the new boss and resigned. He was no more than fifty when Steinegger died.'

'And where is he now?' asked George.

'I don't know. He used to live in the 9th District. Maybe he is still there.'

Pellicio was sent to the 9th District to talk with head waiters in the local coffee-houses, whose duty it is to know everything that goes on. It took Pellicio but three hours and eight cups of coffee to find Herr Tinderer. In the afternoon, George climbed up the four steep flights of stairs to Tinderer's flat, where an eye gazing through a peep-hole in the door answered the bell. A key was turned and the door opened a fraction, to be held by a safety chain. A worried face looked through the slit and asked in a high-pitched voice what George wanted.

'Are you Herr Tinderer?' said George.

'What do you want of him?' the man retorted.

'I am Prince Lahovary,' said George. 'Can I come in or do you like discussing business in public?'

The safety chain was removed and George entered a dimly-lit lobby. He faced a little man with greying hair and an imposing Francis Joseph beard, wearing a velvet house-jacket and carpet slippers. On his nose was a pair of steel-rimmed glasses. He led his visitor into an untidy living-room filled with the smell of stale cabbage. Herr Tinderer pointed to a battered sofa and they sat down.

'I just want to know the answers to a few questions,' said George easily. 'I am willing to pay you five hundred kroner for the information.'

'That is a lot of money, sir,' said Tinderer and shook his head. 'What information can I give you that is that valuable? Is it about the bank? I am afraid, then, I cannot tell you anything.'

'Oh, yes, Herr Tinderer,' said George firmly. 'You can.'
And when the book-keeper shook his head again: 'There are
other ways and means to get the information, but then you
would be five hundred kroner the poorer. And it would not
be pleasant for you.'

Tinderer threw up his hands. 'I can't, I can't,' he cried.
'Leave me alone, please!'

'Won't you tell me why you retired?'

'M-m-my age . . .' he stuttered.

'Come again, Herr Tinderer,' laughed George. 'You are
still a young man. There are older ones working in banks.'

'Madame thought I was too old. She wants younger men,
especially in the book-keeping, to modernize it.'

'Are you telling me that Madame sacked the entire staff?'

'Gradually, sir,' he said. 'We all received a lump sum,
and were told to live in the provinces!'

'So she made them leave Vienna! Why are *you* still here?'

Tinderer shrugged. 'I ought to be in Graz, but I own this
house, so I am staying here as long as I can.'

'Well, Herr Tinderer, one more question . . . and I want
the truth! What is wrong with the books?'

Tinderer went pale. 'Sir,' he asked, 'are you accusing
me?'

'No, no, Herr Tinderer,' said Manolesco, 'I am not
accusing you.' But Tinderer would not give any more
answers, much as George pressed him. After ten minutes
George stormed from the room and was half down the stairs
when Tinderer called down over the bannister: 'Are you the
police?'

George looked up, laughing. 'No, I am not the police!
I am the man who wants to give you five hundred kroner,
remember? I just want to know about one special account.'

'What account?' asked Tinderer in a whisper.

'The sisters Wunderer in Lucerne . . .'

'Never heard the name,' said Tinderer, but too quickly.

George turned round and continued to walk down the
stairs. He heard the door of the flat upstairs shut and the key
being turned. In front of the house he hailed a passing *fiaker*
and gave the coachman the address of Freddy Katz, his

associate and one of Vienna's top crooked lawyers. George
believed that Tinderer was not as shocked or harmless as he
pretended. Taking Freddy with him, he explained the situation as they drove to the Graben corner and stopped where
they could watch the Spiegelgasse. Within ten minutes
Tinderer arrived, walking towards the premises of
Steinegger & Co. As he passed the coach, Freddy stepped
out into the street, produced a small card and showed it to
Tinderer. Without a word the book-keeper followed the
'police inspector' to the waiting carriage. Then he saw
George and stopped dead.

'I told you there are other ways and means of finding
out,' said George coldly. 'It's up to you. Do you want to
talk to me privately, or do you want the Inspector to take
you to headquarters?'

Tinderer trembled. 'There is nothing to talk about,' he
said. 'But if you wish, I will answer your questions . . . if I
can. Only, not the police.'

'All right, Herr Inspector,' said Manolesco. 'I am not
charging the man yet. I believe he will be quite reasonable
now. Many thanks for your assistance.' Freddy, who had in
his day been cashiered from the army, still retained his
military bearing. He saluted stiffly, gave a slight bow, and
walked off. George took Tinderer to the Hotel Kummer,
rode up in the lift with him to his room on the third floor,
and ordered coffee from the floor waiter. Slowly and reluctantly Tinderer talked.

Steinegger & Co. had in trust money for the Imperial
Ottoman Bank, which was due for payment. But there was
no cash in the strong-room, for Michael Steinegger's demands
on money were even bigger than the substantial profits of
his business. He had lost millions of kroner in gambling and
foolish speculation. It was Tinderer's duty to 'correct' the
books so that the auditors could not discover the deficit.

'You see,' explained Tinderer, 'we arranged to have a
robbery! If three million kroner was stolen from our bank,
every other bank in Vienna would come to the rescue of the
victim.'

Two Polish burglars were hired by Michael Steinegger,

three million kroner was 'stolen', together with some 'inconvenient' books containing private accounts. It was just after that that Michael Steinegger died and his wife took over.

'And you cooked the books for Michael,' remarked George. 'Why did you do it, Tinderer? You seem to me to be an honest man. What hold had Steinegger over you?'

It took all George's persuasive abilities to extract the story. Thirty years ago Tinderer had been involved in a political brawl in Prague and had seriously wounded an Austrian officer. Steinegger learned of it, told Tinderer that the officer had died, and offered the young man a job at his bank. 'From then on I had to do what he wanted me to do,' concluded the book-keeper. 'If he had denounced me, I would have been condemned to death.'

'But Madame sent you away?'

'Yes,' nodded Tinderer. 'I left. It did not matter any more. I hated the job, anyway.'

'All right, Tinderer,' said George. 'It was very wise of you to tell me all this and you can rest assured that there will be not the slightest trouble for you. Are you in need of money?'

'No, I have the income from the house and regular money from Madame.'

'Are you married?'

'My wife died ten years ago, sir.'

George took out his wallet, counted out five hundred-kroner notes and gave them to the book-keeper. 'Stay away from the bank,' he said. 'Close your flat, and go to the country until things blow over here. Let me have your address, and I will get in touch with you.' As he escorted the man to the door, George said cheerfully: 'Your worries are over! Good-bye.'

That was where George Manolesco was utterly wrong.

*   *   *

When George left the hotel next morning, he discovered that he was being followed by the young book-keeper from

Steinegger & Co. A few blocks farther along the busy Mariahilferstrasse George turned to face him, but the man had disappeared. Then a headline on a midday paper at a newsvendor's stand caught his eye:

BANK CLERK SERIOUSLY WOUNDED

Tinderer, said the story, had been attacked by unknown persons near his home in the Alserdistrict, hit over the head, and robbed of his money. He was taken to hospital unconscious and was in a grave condition.

'So,' thought George. 'Madame has decided to fight.' If they had taken care of Tinderer, they might soon try to deal with him. He returned to the Hotel Kummer, paid his bill and asked for his luggage to be kept until called for. He left by a back entrance, took a carriage, and booked in again at the Hotel Sacher under the name of Prince Lahovary.

With Freddy's help, he next discovered that Madame repeatedly took a *fiaker* from the bank to an unknown destination. The young clerk whom Freddy's friends had kidnapped for an hour or two, explained that these journeys took place whenever important decisions were to be taken at the bank.

'Madame has explained,' he said, feeling very important to be the centre of so much attention, 'that it is impossible for her to concentrate in the bank with visitors coming and going. She needs fresh air for a clear brain.'

It would have been useless to ask a Viennese *fiaker*-driver for the destination of a passenger—he would never reveal it. So a close watch was kept on the bank until, on the fourth day, Freddy learned that Madame had driven out of Vienna to 'The Retreat', a well-known private sanatorium for wealthy people, and had stayed the night there. Freddy was well acquainted with Dr. Brenner, medical director of 'The Retreat'. Here, in a huge mansion near Lainz, George and Freddy were ushered into the presence of Dr. Brenner. But he had 'no knowledge' of any nocturnal visits from a lady. 'My guests,' he said smiling, 'are beyond the age for night-time adventures. You must be mistaken.'

As they took their leave they decided to question the gate-keeper.

'Did you,' asked George, 'see a carriage arrive here last night?'

The man shook his head. He was a very tall man with a long black beard, a grey top hat, and a gold-embroidered tunic, black breeches and riding boots. A sudden thought struck George. 'How long have you been on this job?' he asked.

'Why do you want to know?' was the defiant answer. The gate-keeper was now standing near the carriage door and George could get a good look at him. He saw the black, shifty eyes, and suddenly flung open the carriage door and jumped out.

'You are Michael Steinegger!' shouted George. 'I would know you anywhere!'

For a second the gate-keeper was thunder-struck. Then he lifted his arm to strike George, but Freddy was quicker. He drew a huge pistol and pointed it at the man. 'Stand still,' he ordered. The gate-keeper obeyed and stared furiously at them. His top hat had fallen off.

'You should not have worn the top hat,' said George, as with the help of the startled coachman and Freddy he dragged Steinegger into the carriage.

In Freddy's office they extracted a full confession from Steinegger. An Italian tourist on the Semmering had been killed in an accident and Steinegger had discovered the body and changed clothes with the man. 'The Retreat', owned by Steinegger & Co., was the ideal hiding-place. He became the gate-keeper and was able to see everybody entering or leaving the mansion. He was not only in an ideal position to spot police should they approach the mansion, but was easily available to give his wife business advice.

Steinegger was bundled again into a carriage and brought to the Hotel Sacher, and to Prince Lahovary's suite. Madame was urgently summoned to the hotel. When she saw her husband, all her resistance crumbled. She went back to the bank with George and Freddy and handed over two suitcases packed with banknotes. She made out a transfer of 100,000 kroner to Freddy and his associates for their work and expenses. And gave George 10,000 kroner for Tinderer.

She wept as she handed over the suitcases. 'We are ruined now, indeed,' she said. 'Here are two million gold francs. Please . . . you must give me back some of it.'

But George was adamant. 'You are still far better off than the two old ladies you cheated!'

George felt for once like a knight in shining armour, a Sir Galahad and Robin Hood rolled into one. He enjoyed every righteous moment. He returned with Pellicio to Zürich the next day and went at once to Ileana.

'It was all a mistake,' he said. 'Your five hundred thousand francs are safe—in fact Michael made such good investments that they have doubled. I have asked Madame Steinegger to transfer your money to a Swiss bank, where an account will be opened for you tomorrow.'

'Thank you very much, George,' said Ileana. 'You have taken a lot of trouble for me, I am sure. You see, I was right. Michael could not do anything wrong! He was always such a good and considerate boy. Don't you agree, George?'

George nodded his head seriously, and said he agreed.

Chapter 9

The responsibility of carrying two suitcases with cash and negotiable bonds worth some two million francs from Vienna to Zürich had made even George a little uneasy and he was glad when he could rid himself of one case by depositing half of the money to the account of Ileana at the Swiss Bank Union. Now he was sitting at the window of his sitting-room in the Hotel Baur au Lac, to pay Pellicio his share of what was left. On the small table before him, neatly bundled, were £50,000 in francs, which he pushed over to the valet, who stared incredulously at the pile of notes.

'I suppose,' said George grinning, 'you will now retire, buy yourself the vineyard you dream about, find a nice girl, marry, and produce both wine and children?'

'No,' replied Pellicio. 'I don't think I will . . . unless you wish to get rid of me! I am still much too young for wine, except for drinking the stuff, and as for marriage, why should I spoil my fun with all the rest for the sake of one? Besides, I detest children! I'll put the money in the bank.'

'The lot?' asked George doubtfully.

'Yes,' answered Pellicio. 'Practically all of it. I'll give my sister in Ajaccio a nice little present, and my mother's brother, poor chap, can have the five thousand francs he always wanted to buy a house, and could never save from the miserable salary they pay an honest teacher in the Third Republic. . . .'

George laughed approvingly. 'The thrifty Frenchman with the soft heart for the family. And for yourself?'

'Nothing,' shrugged Pellicio. 'What do I need? With your

permission, I will get drunk one evening and then have a vacation in Paris. I hope you can manage alone for a week or so?'

'I think I can,' answered George, 'if you tell me where I may find my cuff-links.'

That evening Prince Lahovary and his valet boarded the night express for Paris. There they parted. Pellicio took a room in a small hotel and George continued his journey north to catch the boat for England. He deposited his money-filled suitcase in the cloakroom of the Gare du Nord, told Pellicio to sell or give away his other trunks, cases and contents, and with the relatively paltry sum of £5,000 in his pocket, landed the next morning at Newhaven with only a small handcase. He made straight for London. His wardrobe needed refreshing, and there was no better place in the world than England where they made the finest suits, shirts and shoes for real gentlemen. However, he arrived in the capital at a most unfortunate moment for him. The city was in an uproar. It was the morning of June 20, 1897, only two days before Queen Victoria's Diamond Jubilee. George found himself stranded in the greatest city of the world, gaily decorated, in festive mood, and with seemingly not the slightest chance of securing any kind of accommodation. To sleep in a tent in Hyde Park did not appeal to him, a bench on the Embankment—as suggested by a superior hall porter at the Savoy Hotel—did not meet with approval either. Then he remembered the membership card of the Jockey Club in Vienna, which he carried in his pocket, and the affiliation with London clubs. He presented himself at Crockford's Club asking for help and shelter. An over-worked secretary found a place for him and he was billeted at a member's home in Forest Hill, a south-eastern suburb then populated by wealthy city people. He was taken by his host to the Jubilee Dinner at the Carlton Hotel on the eve of the great day, and on June 22 he watched the pomp and glamour of the Jubilee Procession from a private box in the Mall.

It was the man-about-town son of a peer who introduced Prince Lahovary to other members and other clubs as the scion of an old noble Romanian family, who owned huge estates near Ploesti, and who liked a game of cards. George was considered a charming and well-mannered man, rather amusing with his queer Continental manners, and he became very popular. He was always ready to lend a small sum to a fellow member and obviously dismissed the debt from his mind at once. He was most accommodating! He stayed a week in London, winning moderate sums at the nightly card game, sometimes with a little 'help' on his part, but mostly by simple good play. He went to a highly recommended tailor in Saville Row whose list of clients read like the *Almanach de Gotha*, to get down to the serious business of dress. But this was England and not the Continent and ordering a suit was, to put it mildly, difficult. The tailor explained that scores of foreign rulers, noblemen and other eminent visitors for the Jubilee had the same idea as Prince Lahovary and there was not the slightest chance of an appointment for the first fitting in under two months. There would be four fittings at least. Disgusted, George told this to his host, a city banker of German extraction.

'My dear Prince,' answered the banker, 'it does not surprise me. You cannot hurry an English tailor. But if you are really in a rush, I'll give you an introduction to my own man, a Czech Jew in the East End of London, who will do what you want within a week, and at a fraction of Saville Row prices.'

'But Saville Row . . . !' objected George, disappointed. The banker reassured him: 'Not all English suits come from Saville Row, my dear Prince. I know at least a dozen peers who order them from my little tailor.'

Jankoff Abramovitch, a hunchbank, received with delight the order to produce twenty different suits to cover all occasions for Prince Lahovary, with but one fitting and delivery within ten days. True, he raised the price to seven guineas a suit and took fifty pounds on account to buy the materials selected. George, still sceptical, decided to accept meantime an invitation from one of his young noble friends to spend a week at a country house-party—and never forgot his one and only sojourn in a genuine English mansion as a guest of a real lord. 'I had to buy myself a dinner jacket off the peg, but it fitted; tweed suit, riding breeches, and rain-wear—which did not fit. That did not matter, nobody's clothes fitted. The company was so blue-blooded that I was afraid to cut myself while shaving and so disclose that Prince Lahovary had ordinary red blood. At least a dozen lords and a few odd baronets were mingled with a Cabinet Minister, a German Prince, and a Dowager Duchess related to Queen Victoria—and all recovering from the Jubilee junketing. At the week-end a dozen debutantes and their escorts arrived for a dance, and the ballroom glittered with diadems and necklaces that made Fontana's in Paris look like a junk-shop.'

There was every opportunity to steal, but George restrained himself. He realized that jewels disappearing in this company would create a colossal scandal. He did not believe that the draught-hardened Englishwomen—world famed for frigidity—would keep as silent as their Continental sisters. Besides, every guest knew that two detectives from Scotland Yard had accompanied the Cabinet Minister and the German Prince, and George had heard so much of the efficiency of Scotland Yard that he preferred to endure the tantalizing situation and stay remembered in England as a perfect gentleman. The alternative would only be a long spell in jail. 'That,' he told Pellicio, 'would not have been fair to my tailor. I would lose weight in prison.'

He returned to London after the week-end and took a suite in the enormous Northumberland Hotel just by Trafalgar Square. Mr. Abramovitch was as good as his word. Three days after the fitting he delivered the entire wardrobe in person at the hotel and proudly pointed out to his client the little label sewn on to an inside pocket of each jacket, bearing the name and address of one of the most famous Saville Row tailors. At George's look of surprise he said with a chuckle: 'I work for them, making their trousers. So I can get the labels. So I sewed them into your suits. It looks better than Jankoff Abramovitch.' George agreed and paid the balance due very willingly.

'Thank you,' said the little hunchback. 'This will help to

put me up in business in the West End. When you come back to London, Mister Highness, don't forget "Jan Amos", that's me, bespoke tailor of Vigo Street. It was a pleasure to work for you, sir.'

George gave him an extra ten pounds, promised to patronize Jan Amos's establishment, and went to Burlington Arcade to buy shirts, underwear, collars and ties. With ten pieces of luggage he left London two days later for Paris, wearing his new green-grey travelling suit with deer-stalker cap.

But at Dover he changed his mind. After all the dull—and financially profitless—days in England, he was longing for some excitement, a real flutter at the tables for example; so he made straight for Brussels, to compensate for the 'fan-tastically bad food', as he put it, that he had endured for the last three weeks. He had a gourmet's meal at the Hotel Metropole, and left next morning for the gaming tables of Spa in southern Belgium.

He was, however, so completely out of luck that within three days the last of the £5,000 he had started with had been lost at roulette. He had barely enough to pay his—as usual—steep hotel bill, buy a first-class ticket to Paris, dispatch his luggage, and send a wire to Pellicio to meet him at the Gare du Nord. He arrived in the afternoon with fifty francs in his pocket.

A beaming Pellicio stood at the barrier and paid the porters and the carriage to the hotel. 'I reserved a suite for Your Highness,' he announced, 'at the new Elysée Palace Hôtel near the Pont d'Alma. Three rooms on the second floor with bath and a telephone in the sitting-room—with a smaller room for the valet. I hope Your Highness is satisfied.'

'Very much,' said George approvingly. 'But who the hell do I telephone from the room?'

His Highness's own English clothes met with the complete approval of the valet but not the black bowler hat and two pairs of striped trousers George had brought back for his faithful associate. 'Must I run around like a monkey?' he asked George. George shook his head. 'Only on great occasions,' he answered, 'such as when I give a party—which I might even do one day.'

The next morning, when George for the first time in nearly a month had breakfast off his own silver and porcelain, Pellicio appeared with the tray, garbed in striped trousers, black jacket, black tie . . . and wearing his bowler hat. George roared with laughter and told him to change into ordinary clothes at once.

After retrieving the suitcase of money from the Gare du Nord, George considered his next move. The débâcle in Spa and his previous losses at roulette only convinced him that he should launch at once a serious and, he hoped, successful campaign against the treacherous wheel. With a fortune to back him, it seemed possible to beat the obstinate machine; it might prove the finest of all the *coups* of the Great Manolesco.

Pellicio brought the Frenchman's natural caution to bear. 'And if it goes wrong?' he asked.

'You are a born pessimist,' said George. 'What *should* go wrong? If we are short of money we can always find a little card game to correct such a state of affairs, or perhaps a lovely blonde, maybe a redhead, with a pearl necklace for Carcola.'

For two months Prince Lahovary and Pellicio travelled the casinos and gambling houses of the Côte d'Azur. Nearly everywhere, however, the wheel stayed undefeated, and losses mounted higher and higher.

'I think that soon I'll have to lend you money, George,' remarked Pellicio one morning in Cannes, when the hotel bill was overdue—thus emphasizing delicately that the valet, at least, remained wealthy. But George had a little *tête-à-tête* with the wife of an Algerian Government official and acquired a set of sapphires and rubies, for which Carcola paid him 20,000 francs.

By the end of 1897, however, the Nice police had received so many complaints of heavy losses at one of the many private gambling circles in town, that, bad as it was for the tourist trade, they had to raid the establishment. Thirty ladies and gentlemen were rounded up, taken to the Police

Headquarters, booked and searched. Those who could identify themselves were sent home, the majority remained at the *préfecture*. Among them was 'Monsieur George Manolesco', fearful lest the name Prince Lahovary should somehow leak out. Apart from a large sum of money, a pearl necklace had been found in his pocket and despite all his indignant protests and although no one had reported such a necklace stolen, the *Préfet de Police* simply did not believe that George had won it in a game, and kept him in jail for further investigation. When the news reached Pellicio in the morning, he hired the best lawyer in town, paid the hotel and left for Marseilles on the next train, with all their luggage, to wait for his master at Carcola's.

It took four weeks for even the clever lawyer to get his client released on bail of 1,000 francs. George, reverting to his princely status, joined Pellicio, who observed that he was slightly slimmer than a month before. Donning one of his new English suits at the Hôtel de Louvre in Marseilles, George commented: 'Anyway, my little rest cure helped to improve my line. Everything has a good and a bad side,' and went out with Carcola for a bouillabaisse 'Chez Henri' in the rue Pavillion. He only regretted that the Nice police had retained the pearl necklace.

The next few weeks he preferred to stay out of France entirely and travelled east. After his first bad impression of Vienna, several years ago, he had developed quite a liking for the gay city on the Danube, and began his tour there; then to Budapest, Prague, and to the Bohemian spas of Marienbad, Karlsbad and Teplitz, just then coming very much into fashion. At the roulette tables he lost constantly, but made up his losses with cards and thefts from unlocked hotel rooms. But the pickings in the Austrian spas were minute compared with those from the wealthy women of the South of France and early in 1898 he was back in Monte Carlo and once more at the roulette tables. To beat the odds, by hook or by crook, became an obsession with him.

When the season ended in June, he discovered to his surprise that his war against the wheel had reduced his assets of £250,000 to a mere £3,500, and decided to give the tables a rest. He travelled to Switzerland and stayed a few days in Lucerne's Hotel National. But Lucerne was full of sad memories for George, every stone reminded him of the fortune squandered within a year, and he ordered Pellicio to pack their trunks once more. They took the express to Milan. Italy was still maiden territory for George.

*   *   *

The two ladies travelling in a compartment next to George were intriguing and evidently of some quality. The younger one he estimated at twenty-five years of age; she was dressed in an expensively simple travelling costume; her figure was not striking but good enough, her features not beautiful but regular. She had fluffy, dark hair, held in place by a silk scarf fastened with a knot under her chin. Her hands were well kept but rather plump. The feet showing beneath the long sweeping dress were wonderfully shod, but rather large. George, connoisseur of feminine beauty, classified her at first as a wallflower grown in the dull surroundings of a large farming estate, more at home with horses, cows and pigs than in the world of society. But when he saw her blue eyes, large and radiant, he revised his estimate, and decided she was definitely attractive.

Her chaperone was an elderly lady, rather more heavily made-up, with lace frills on her blouse, half a dozen rings on her fingers and a string of pearls around her neck. She seemed to be a southerner—either Italian or Spanish—and had a lean, small face, and sleek black hair.

In the privacy of their compartment, Pellicio asked George: 'Have you seen the necklace? Seems to be good stuff. A bit old-fashioned, perhaps; maybe it is a family heirloom, or perhaps her wedding present?'

George shrugged. 'Not exactly in our line,' he answered. 'Small pearls do not fetch a good price. And they are not too well matched either. Too commonplace for Carcola. But the girl is not so bad, though perhaps also a bit old-fashioned.'

'Mother and daughter?' asked Pellicio.

'Most likely,' nodded George. 'We'll find out soon.'

When the express emerged from the long journey through the St. Gotthard tunnel and into the southern sun, the acquaintance of the ladies was made in the corridor of the coach. They told George that they were on a journey through Italy and would stay for a few days at the Hotel Cavour in Milan before going on to Florence and Rome. George presented one of his PRINCE LAHOVARY cards and announced that he too would be staying at the Cavour. 'I would be honoured to be of service to you,' he said in his most engaging manner. 'My valet is at your disposal, to help with your luggage and carriage.'

As the train slowly rolled into the station at Lugano for a brief halt, he sent Pellicio to the telegraph office to make a reservation at the Cavour and to cancel that at the Hotel Continental.

The two ladies, who had introduced themselves as Baroness von Koenigsbrueck and daughter Angelika, gracefully accepted the aid of the charming Prince and together they drove to the hotel, leaving Pellicio in charge of all the luggage. It was clear to George that the young Baroness Angelika found great pleasure in his company, and—despite some reserve and perhaps a little scepticism—Mamma also seemed to like him.

After a short rest, George invited the ladies to a sight-seeing tour in his newly-hired private carriage and then to a lavish supper in a restaurant in the arcades of the Piazza del Duomo. At midnight George brought the ladies back to the hotel, kissed Angelika's hand, bowed most politely to her mother and made an appointment for the next morning. Then he went to his suite to console a fuming Pellicio; George suggested they should go out and discover Milan. Pellicio knew the city well, especially the shady side with its maze of alleys directly behind the Cathedral and the Royal Palace, consisting of hundreds of wine-shops and bordellos; he even found George a gambling-place in the Viale Piave, frequented by young men of good family with too much money and chronic insomnia. Here George won 2,000 lire in a card game and Pellicio commented: 'If you intend to travel with a harem you probably will need the money!' They returned to the hotel in the small hours of the morning, but George was down at the hall at ten for his appointment and took his new friends on an excursion to nearby Como in the Alps, with lunch at the lakeside. The next day Mamma suffered from terrible migraine, so Angelika and George strolled together through the city on a shopping expedition. This ended with an intimate supper at Alfonso's, the most famous eating-house in Milan. In the gay, heady atmosphere of the small but exquisite restaurant, Angelika made no bones about the fact that she had fallen in love with Prince Charming. George did his best to stay dispassionate, although he later told Pellicio that after a few glasses of wine, and in her delicately-coloured evening gown, he found the Baroness almost attractive. He summed it up: 'She was definitely in love with me, but I found her only *sympathique.*'

When they left Alfonso's, Angelika insisted that George should send the carriage away so that they could walk to the hotel through the badly-lit streets, 'like two real lovers'. When they settled on a bench in the small park opposite the hotel Angelika began to talk about herself. She came from a noble family in Saxonia, 'but unfortunately not a rich one. We are very poor, George. . . .'

Here he interrupted her: 'That does not matter if one is as beautiful as you are!' and kissed her. She made no protest but then said quietly and mockingly: 'I am an old girl, George! I am twenty-eight. So, if you are serious with your kisses, you ought to know that you would not only get a wife without money, but also an elderly one.'

'I do not care how old you are and how little money you have,' George said quite warmly. 'I have plenty, my oil interests alone yield more than fifty thousand francs a year, not to speak of my companies in France. I would never marry you for your money, my darling!'

The next morning, George in morning coat and armed with a gigantic bunch of flowers, was announced at the room of Madame, and asked for the hand of her daughter. His request was received politely but hardly with enthusiasm. However, she gave her consent, but said it was necessary to consult Angelika's brother who was on his estate in Germany. When a telegraphic assent arrived later that evening, it was time to inform Pellicio of the pending change in George's life. The Corsican shook his head sadly. 'You, a married man?' he exclaimed. 'The girl has no money, she is not a beauty and besides she is a Boche! What is your reason? To seduce her? You could jump into bed with her at any time. What do you expect to get from such a marriage?'

A few moments later Pellicio took up the subject again. 'You told me you did not want the girl in Chicago, although she had oceans of money,' he protested. 'I could quite understand that. But now, are you tired of life and fed up with excitement, or have you just gone soft?'

'I knew you would not approve of her,' said George. 'But it is not you but I who is to marry her. She is a fine girl and she is a perfect lady, from a first-class family. Does Prince Lahovary not deserve a perfect lady? As her husband I would become a member of her family and that is worth some inconveniences. We will find some money if necessary. She wishes to marry me, can I refuse a lady's wishes? I am burning to make the acquaintance of my new circle of noble and exalted relations. One day, I am sure I might be introduced to the Kaiser, which might be an amusing experience!'

'Or you will be caught,' snapped Pellicio sourly—he had no love for the German Kaiser.

George laughed. 'Caught? So what? Nobody would harm me even if I were caught—as you so bluntly put it. If that happened my new family would raise heaven and earth to hush things up. They would never let the world know they had such a family skeleton as me. It is, in fact, an insurance policy!'

They were married on December 17, 1898 at the Romanian Consulate in Genoa, George with brand-new papers, acquired for 5,000 francs and with Carcola's help; they were in the name of George Mercadente Manolesco. He adjusted a little 'oversight' by adding the two letters P and R before the names, thus retaining his princely status for the benefit of his new family. He explained to the Consul that the letters meant he was the first born son of his father! The Consul did not care one way or the other. To Angelika George explained that 'Manolesco' was the name of a branch of the Lahovarys, and frequently used by them. It was as simple as that.

The couple started their honeymoon at the Hotel Isotta in the Via Roma in Genoa. George showered his young wife with luxuries, he even *bought* her jewels.

Angelika, who had been used to the sober atmosphere of a impecunious Junker's life, was deliriously happy. Her mother, alas, was not. A strong believer in the Roman Catholic Church, she insisted that a priest must solemnize the marriage, which presented George with a serious problem. Angelika was Catholic, George was Greek Orthodox—and Rome did not like the alliance. George had solved complicated problems before. Now he was received in a private audience by the Archbishop of Genoa, Salvadore Magnasco, a kind-hearted man who was grateful for a substantial donation from the charming Romanian nobleman, and invited Prince Lahovary, his young bride and her mother to tea at his Palace, promising to give the young couple his blessing in his private chapel. This was a neat evasion of the issue but it satisfied Madame von Koenigsbrueck and restored her peace of mind. With Mamma in tow the couple moved on to the Hotel Quirinale in Rome.

George was troubled at this time—not by his marriage to Angelika von Koenigsbrueck, but by his rapidly dwindling funds, which upon arrival in Rome had reached the low level of about £1,000. Something had to be done if he wished to continue the princely style of living, impressing his new relations, showering mother-in-law with presents, and his wife with flowers, clothes and jewels. The suite at the hotel, the hired private carriage, and the wages of the groom and a personal maid for his wife brought his daily expenses to the uncomfortable total of seventy-five pounds.

Pellicio, having met a sweet little French maid at the Hotel Continental, and feeling that George had bitten off slightly more than he could chew, came to the rescue with news of a good 'prospect' in the Continental. On the fourth day of their stay in Rome, George, in one of his

London-made suits and Panama hat, walked across to the Continental, while his wife and her mother visited their hotel hairdresser. As brazenly as ever he went up by lift to the fourth floor, tipped the lift-man generously, and then slowly descended the staircase to the third floor. He found five rooms unlocked and four of them yielded a rich haul. He returned unchallenged to his hotel an hour later and showed the results of his little expedition to Pellicio. They consisted of a package of twenty-five American $100 bills, held together with thin string, a small diadem of diamonds and pearls, worth perhaps £2,000, two bracelets of sapphires and rubies, a single string of pearls, and a diamond brooch mounted in gold.

'Bless the Grand Hotels,' he said, smiling at Pellicio. 'They are the same all over the world. If you enter with a million francs in your pocket but a hole in your jacket, they will probably kick you out. But wear a smart suit, patent-leather shoes and an air of belonging, and they won't ask you whether you have a centime to your name. They will even bow you out of the place when you are ready to leave.

It was agreed that Pellicio would go to Marseilles next morning to exchange the jewels for cash, and with his wallet fattened by £500 in good American money, George took the ladies for a drive on the Janiculum Hill and supper at the Villa Borghese.

Pellicio's departure was nearly delayed, however. George, up early as usual, had gone to the sitting-room of the suite to study the newspapers. His excursion to the Hotel Continental had received fair publicity, accusing the management of negligence and stupidity. The final paragraph reported that among the gems stolen was a diamond brooch owned by a young lady who had come to Rome to see one of the city's most celebrated doctors. *She had lost her sight in an accident a few months previously.* The brooch was her only reminder of her dead mother.

Pellicio smiled sardonically when he read the paragraph. But George shook his head seriously. He took the brooch from the small heap of jewellery on the escritoire and stared at it.

'We will return this,' he said. 'I do not like stealing from a blind girl, or robbing her of her memories.' He wrapped the brooch in a piece of paper, sat down, and wrote a note apologizing for taking the brooch and wishing the young lady every success in her consultation with the doctor. He did not sign the letter. Pellicio was dispatched to the Hotel Continental to deliver it to the hall porter, and had to rush from there to the station to catch the train to the north with the rest of the loot.

They met again in Naples a week later when Pellicio brought the now urgently needed funds, stayed a few days on Capri, took the night boat to Palermo and journeyed across Sicily to Taormina. When the weather deteriorated and George's money was again at low ebb, it was decided to visit the estate of Angelika's brother in Saxonia, he having invited them to stay with him until they found a home of their own.

They arrived at the end of February 1899, a cold and snowy winter, and the two brothers-in-law met for the first time. Baron Ernst Georg August Wilding von Koenigs-brueck, stiff, correct and very formal, took an instant dislike to the Romanian Prince, largely because Pellicio made it very plain that *he* did not like any Germans, but especially disliked Prussians and Saxonians. Neither could George stand his brother-in-law, who lacked the slightest sense of humour; who had no understanding of the niceties of life and the importance of being well dressed, but spent all day in a pair of leather breeches, wellington boots and a high-necked shooting jacket. He did not even wear a clean shirt underneath. The baronial house was a rambling mansion, miles from any civilization, and in the middle of potato- and corn-fields, now an endless desert of snow bordered by dense forest. His wife, *née* Maria von Klenck, was lean, chinless and unsmiling. She wore a pince-nez. The estate had been hers before they married.

The bedrooms were comfortable enough, with huge four-poster beds and overstuffed feather covers, but the ballroom was now degraded to a kind of store room, and the only room which aimed at anything like luxury was the small *salon* always well heated, but overcrowded with plush sofas and leather chairs, each with its crocheted antimacassar. Family portraits of Prussian and Saxonian officers adorned the walls, under them stood glass cases of porcelain, military medals, daggers, pistols and swords. It was a dull, unimaginative house, typical of a Junker. When freshly baked rolls were served in the morning-room on scratched blue-bordered pottery, with weak coffee in thick, chipped cups, Angelika caught the disapproving look on her husband's face. 'They do not care,' she said apologetically, 'but I will tell Mother to get the good china out for you, George.'

George kissed her and shook his head. 'Never mind,' he said. 'It is quite all right, darling.'

Angelika was not convinced, and rather disturbed by the freely expressed comments of her husband's valet. 'You know, George,' she said, 'why do you not use your own crockery? Pellicio has unpacked it, he has even repolished the silver.'

'No,' was George's answer. 'But what I will do is to give the whole outfit to your brother. Do you think he will accept it as a gift from me?'

The Baron accepted willingly the more-than-generous gift from his brother-in-law and to show his appreciation, invited his neighbours and friends from as far away as Dresden and Leipzig to a grand dance as soon as the snow melted.

Preparations began at once: a small army of estate workers, reinforced by two carpenters from the village, put the ballroom and dining-room in reasonable shape; chairs and tables were borrowed from the town hall of the market town; and on March 31 Prince Lahovary was formally introduced to local society—Guards officers from the entourage of the Kaiser and the King of Saxonia, baronesses and countesses, and relations from distant branches of the clan of Koenigsbrueck, Baron Palombini, who had married his wife's sister Auguste Marie, the French relations and the cousins from Alsace-Lorraine, and the Italian and Bavarian uncles and aunts, as well as the famous Trzebinskis from the other side of the Vistula River. The party, preceded by a hunt, was a great success, and so was George, much to the relief of Angelika. Both were invited to all the nearby estates.

George had other plans. He announced that he would buy a house for Angelika and himself in South Germany, and that to settle some business affairs he would have to go to Paris and Switzerland, but would return in a fortnight.

In fact his money was finished; also both his brother-in-law and his mother-in-law had began to ask most embarrassing questions. One relation had mentioned that he had never heard of a 'Prince Lahovary' and asked if the Koenigsbruecks knew anything about the family. They did not, but were determined to find out, going so far as to insist that George should produce a proper family tree, so that the marriage could be registered in the German Index of Nobility and be entered in the *Almanach de Gotha*. George promised to produce his family-tree and left for France.

In only three weeks' time he had enough money to return to Germany and buy his home—if he wanted to. The chance to acquire a lot more money than he had expected came the day after his arrival at the Hôtel des Anglais in Monte Carlo.

Chapter 10

Pellicio, in blue serge suit and black tie, disapprovingly took the breakfast tray from the floor waiter, shook his head over the shocking state of the hotel silver, and entered his master's *salon*. George sat at the open window, looking out over the blue sea with unseeing eyes—he had a vision of swaying palm trees, and the flower-decked gardens of Hawaii, then a nightmare glimpse of the drab, monotonous landscape of Lower Saxonia. He shuddered.

Pellicio silently laid the table and produced a letter. 'This came half an hour ago, Your Highness,' he announced. George, still absent-minded, took the large, oblong envelope of heavy ivory paper and turned it over in his hands. It was addressed to George Lahovary, at the hotel. He looked questioningly at Pellicio.

'If I were you, George,' said the valet, 'I would open it!'

George took a table knife and slit open the envelope. The single sheet of paper inside was of the same heavy quality, and emblazoned with a red and gold coat-of-arms, under which was the inscription:

THE ROYAL LEGATION OF VALEBIANCO

The signature of His Excellency, Count Nikita Arcidovonci produced a smile on George's lips. Count Nikita was an old acquaintance, a roving diplomat and confidant of the ruler of the State we will call 'Valebianco', high up in the stark Balkan mountains. The letter read:

My dear Georgi,

I heard you arrived in Monte Carlo yesterday evening and would very much like to see you. Could you spare the time to come to my hotel at five in the afternoon? I am looking forward to meeting you again.

Yours Nikki.

George read the letter twice and then passed it over to Pellicio. 'Nikki, of all people,' he said. 'When were we in that mountain wilderness of his?'

'Three years ago,' replied Pellicio.

'Any unpleasantness there?' George asked.

Pellicio shrugged. 'Not to speak of. You tried to correct the cards, but "Dimmi" could do it better than you. You dropped quite a bit of money.'

George laughed and started to attack his breakfast. 'Naturally,' he said. 'He is the greatest card-sharper I have ever met in all my travels!'

George knew Count Nikita from Budapest where he had met him soon after joining up with Pellicio. The Count had been sent to the Hungarian capital to discuss a trade deal over pigs, the main export of Valebianco. Having concluded his negotiations, the Count thought it a pity to leave Budapest for the wilderness without tasting some of the famous night-life of the Danubian capital. After three days he had lost all his money at the tables, and was found by George with a tremendous hangover, in the hall of his hotel. George helped him pay off his gaming debts and his hotel bill and in turn was invited to Valebianco, which suited him excellently as he wished then to be out of circulation for a short time.

The ancestral palace of the Arcidovoncis turned out to be a whitewashed one-storey farm house with a straw roof. It squatted in a mud-covered yard in which a dozen or so pigs squeaked and grunted. The main feature was a big manure heap in front of the french windows of the drawing-room. The yard was fenced in by a low stone wall with a wooden gate leading onto the cobbled main square of the capital, Terinje. Directly opposite stood the Palace of Valebianco's ruler, His Royal Highness, Prince Dimitrov—or 'Dimmi' to his friends. It was also whitewashed and in farm-house style, but had a red roof. It boasted two storeys and two small white towers. The wall surrounding it was adorned with golden-painted spikes, and in front of the wooden gate stood two sentries in colourful uniforms, sleepy-eyed and inert. They were armed with large sticks to discourage stray pigs from entering the palace grounds. On the other sides of the square were about a score of white houses, the homes of the accredited diplomats, ministers and courtiers.

Prince Dimitrov was amusing and witty, shrewd and with great personal charm. He was huge, and as with most fat people, good natured. He nearly always wore the national costume of white, pleated frock coat, gay coloured waistcoat and a tiny pillbox cap. He had succeeded in making his little pig-growing country one of the most important factors in Balkan politics. His quite beautiful daughters had been married off to the rulers of Great Powers, and the unique position of Valebianco, on a rock, dominating the Adriatic, secured him the friendship of Germany, Austria, Italy and Russia. But Valebianco was a poor country and such taxes as could be collected scarcely allowed 'Dimmi' the luxury of a Royal Court, including a French chef of some reputation. Prince Dimmi was always hard up, but because of his good family relations, never found closed doors in the Finance Ministries he approached for State loans.

In his Palace he entertained diplomats, ministers and dis-tinguished visitors in the grand manner every evening, invariably ending with a 'friendly game' in the blue *salon*, to recoup some of the costs. Dimmi and George took a great liking to each other and their friendship was not even marred when George started to cheat fairly blatantly at cards. For Dimmi could cheat better! And he did. He did not object to George's tricks, or even protest. He just countered them with his own specialities and George discovered with horror that His Royal Highness was a far better sharper than himself and that he had been selected to meet most of the entertainment bills of the royal household during his fort-night's visit. When he left he was very lucky that Count

Nikki repaid him the money loaned in Budapest (anyway the greater part of it) to meet the fare to Vienna.

Smilingly remembering the hectic nights at the tables in Terinje, George now wrote a note accepting Nikki's invitation and dispatched Pellicio to the Count's hotel.

When he entered the hotel at five o'clock in the afternoon, Count Nikki was waiting for him in the Winter Garden. He had not changed a bit. He was still the charming, affable *bon vivant*, wearing a grey suit with a large silver star on his left breast, the perfect picture of a Grand Seigneur from the tips of his patent-leather shoes all seven feet up to the half dozen grey hairs on his otherwise bald head. He dropped his monocle when he shook hands with George, let it dangle on its black ribbon, embraced him, and slapped his back. They went to the Count's room for a glass of slivovitz, but for some time Nikki offered no reason why he wanted to see George so suddenly. George, mannered as ever, did not ask but inquired about Terinje and Prince Dimmi, getting the short reply that H.R.H. was very well. It seemed to George that despite his jolly air, Count Nikki was deeply perturbed.

At 7 p.m. a groom entered the room to announce that a carriage was waiting. George stood up to take his leave, but Nikki raised a hand to stay him.

'Would you come with me?' he asked unsmilingly. George agreed, far too curious to decline. Half an hour later, the carriage stopped in front of the Riviera Club, a grey sandstone building in Condamine, outside Monte Carlo. George knew the club well, it was one of the places where nothing was barred and anyone could lose his money without the formality of presenting credentials as demanded by the *Direction* of the Casino.

The half-dozen tables in the dimly-lit room were occupied by the usual crowd, the soft clicking of the roulette wheel rose over the subdued murmur of the gamblers. The curtains were drawn tightly, for sunshine was undesirable. Flunkeys in gold-braided uniforms guarded the doors and kept a careful eye on the visitors.

At one table the crowd of onlookers was bigger than elsewhere. 'Probably someone on a running streak,' thought

George. Then, through a gap in the crowd, he saw His Royal Highness, Prince Dimitrov, absolute ruler of Valebianco, his open peasant's face beaming with pleasure, as well it might be.

Heaps of counters were stacked in front of him, so were several bundles of banknotes. He pushed a huge pile of counters on to red, without counting them, and a gasp went through the crowd at the sight of the fortune staked so casually. The voice of the croupier came monotonously: 'Faites vos jeux, Mesdames, Messieurs. . . . Les jeux sont faits. . . . Rien ne va plus!' All betting stopped, the croupier gave the wheel a small, experienced twist and threw in the little ivory ball. There was silence except for the hypnotic click of the wheel. George felt the old excitement and stared fascinated at the little ball flickering round the wheel. Gradually it slowed, then stopped. The croupier chanted: 'Le vingt deux. . . . Pair, rouge et passe. . . .' Dimmi had doubled his stake. Swiftly the croupier pushed over the Prince's enormous winnings.

Everybody, as if by command, started talking excitedly, only the winner himself seemed unconcerned. George smiled at Nikki. 'He is not doing so badly!'

Again the croupier announced the game. Again, Dimmi pushed an uncounted heap of counters on the table—and won. Again the crowd seethed with excitement at the incredible luck of the royal player.

Then, through the crowd of onlookers a lady approached the table. She was beautiful. With a strikingly pale face, surrounded by blue-black hair, she wore a fashionable lace-covered afternoon dress and her tiny flower-decked straw hat was set at a saucy angle. She smiled at Dimmi, put one arm around his massive shoulders, and opened her large handbag adroitly with her free hand. Without a word being spoken, she collected the counters and the money in front of Dimmi and crammed all into her bag. The crowd stood silent, flabbergasted. The croupier did not move. Dimmi said and did absolutely nothing.

She closed the bag, gave Dimmi a playful pat on the cheek and smiled. 'Thank you, chéri,' she said sweetly. 'I

knew you'd keep your word and let me have all your winnings
for today!' With a wave of her hand and a 'See you later, mon
chéri,' she pushed through the crowd and vanished.

Still Dimmi did not move. He looked down at the few
odd counters left in front of him, raked them together and
pushed them on red. The croupier found his voice and called:
'Faites vos jeux . . .' as if nothing had happened.

Nikki smiled weakly and led George to a quiet corner in
the hall. In nervous, staccato sentences he began to explain.
As so often before, His Royal Highness, glad of a break in the
monotony of life in Valebianco, had gone to Rome for
financial negotiations. He could not stay away from the
gambling tables and lost so much that he not only ran out of
cash but into debt. Nikki had no money, nor had the diplomatic representative of the little Kingdom, who was still
waiting for last year's salary. The latest 'State loan' was
in danger if the truth leaked out, money had to be found.
An Italian friend suggested a money-lender, but the money-
lender was not too eager. The reputation of Valebianco's
ruler was not such as to secure a large sum of money, even
on the security of pigs to be exported to Austria-Hungary! As
H.R.H. was about to leave the offices of the money-lender,
the man pointed at a ring Dimmi wore on his right hand.

'Impossible!' cried H.R.H., deeply shocked. 'This ring
. . . I cannot part with this ring! The political consequences
would be catastrophic!'

The money-lender was unimpressed. He offered to lend
H.R.H. 50,000 francs on security of the ring, and swore that
nobody would ever hear about the transaction. Dimmi took
the ring from his finger and handed it over to the money-
lender.

When he had said that it was of political importance, he
had told only half the story. The ring was a national relic,
the nearest thing to Crown Jewels in Valebianco. It had been
worn by the ruler of the State, ever since Dimmi's great-
grandfather had started his dynasty by killing his competitor
for the throne. Without the ring on his finger, Dimmi dare
not return to Terinje—the outraged population would have
started a revolution.

Dimmi was an inveterate gambler, and was convinced now that with the money lent to him he would regain all his losses, redeem the national heritage, and dodge all his troubles for a while longer. With Nikki he moved on to the Riviera to try his luck. And his luck had changed. Within five days he had made nearly enough money to redeem the ring. Then suddenly all his hopes were destroyed.

One afternoon the valet entered the suite of H.R.H. and announced that a lady wished to speak to him. Dimmi laughed. He had always been a lady's man and as his money worries were nearly over, he considered that a little dalliance might fittingly conclude this trip. The lady was shown in, and she was all Dimmi could have desired. She told him that her name was Mariella and that she was a variety singer. Dimmi was charmed. He called for liqueur and *petits fours* before asking what he could do to be of service to her.

The answer was blunt and to the point. Mademoiselle Mariella knew of the little transaction H.R.H. had concluded a few days ago in Rome! But His Royal Highness need not be alarmed for she had no intention of publicizing the fact, although obviously the Vienna papers would love such a story. Naturally she expected to be compensated for the loss of fees she would have received for the story.

Dimmi nearly died of shock; he saw only scandal, exile and poverty ahead. So, Dimmi paid. But the beautiful blackmailer was not content with what cash Dimmi had available; she wanted far more and since Dimmi's winnings were an open secret in town, she turned up at the Club to help herself—knowing that her victim could say nothing.

'You want me to find a way out of Dimmi's dilemma?' asked George. 'You must have a lot of confidence in me, mon cher Nikki. What guarantee have you got that I, myself, do not use the knowledge of this affair for my own ends?'

Nikki shook his head seriously. 'George,' he said, 'you are making yourself worse than you are. We have heard a lot about you, we know that you are a clever sharper and a swindler, but that is your business. From my own experience I know that you are a gentleman, whatever the . . . ahem . . . rumours say. I would not believe for a single moment that

you would betray the confidence of a friend in distress.' He
smiled winningly at George. 'Besides, you may believe me
that I have not the slightest intention of using the information given to us by our very efficient Chief of Police, that
the much-sought George Manolesco is actually Prince
Lahovary . . . !'

'So, it *is* blackmail,' said George, not in the slightest
put-out. 'However, blackmail does not guarantee my silence.
Besides, I am not a nursemaid to gambling royalty. Dimmi is
quite capable of looking after himself.' He stood up.

'George!' called Nikki, holding him by the arm. 'We must
be drastic! You are the only one I know who can help us
avoid a catastrophe. History will thank you for saving our
beloved Motherland.'

'Very dramatic,' said George drily. 'But Valebianco is
nearer to *your* heart than to mine. . . .'

'Certainly,' answered Nikki, 'but twenty-five thousand
francs in cash might help to bring it nearer to yours?'

George laughed aloud. 'Nikki,' he said, 'you are a bastard
and a scoundrel. You haven't got a centime and yet you
promise me twenty-five thousand francs. But I think you are
also a man of honour, having repaid my loan to you. All
right. I accept. I'll think it over and will try to find a way
out. And do not forget the money!'

George drove back to his hotel and discussed the affair
with Pellicio, who suggested kidnapping the lady and taking
her money, or stealing her jewellery. But George hated
violence, and he also doubted she had enough jewellery to
make it worth while. There always remained the danger that
she would talk. Then it occurred to him that a lady like
Mariella must probably have some dark spots in her past,
and would be well known to certain circles on the Côte
d'Azur. Pellicio soon found out that Madame Mariella's
reputation in Nice was beyond reproach, she lived a relatively blameless life, having a wealthy admirer who was very
lucky at the tables.

'But,' added Pellicio, 'that applies only to Nice, where
she stays at the Hôtel Luxembourg. In Monte, the story is
different. She is very well known here, for she was arrested

for "accidentally lifting" somebody's winnings from the tables. Her victim was a German industrialist, who took Madame's apologies with Teutonic bad grace! The directors of the Casino hushed it up. Madame was given the *viatique*, the free ticket home, her hotel bill was paid by the Casino, and Madame disappeared.'

George smiled. 'Let me think that over,' he said.

The next morning, at seven o'clock, a shabby carriage arrived at the entrance to the Hôtel Luxembourg and four men stepped out on to the gravel of the drive. The big swing doors of the hotel were still closed, so were all the shutters of the guest rooms, and with the exception of a milk-boy and a baker's delivery-man, nobody was in sight. Nice was still fast asleep.

The four men in sober black coats and top hats entered the hotel through a small side door. One of them, a portly and important-looking man, with a small pointed beard, had across his grey waistcoat a broad ribbon with the colours of the *tricolore*. The sleepy night-porter took the visitors to the second floor, where they knocked at the door of Madame's suite. A maid in a flimsy morning gown asked haughtily what was the meaning of this disturbance at such an unbelievable hour.

The man with the beard answered in an official voice. 'I am the *Préfet de Police*! I demand to see Madame Mariella.'

The maid hesitated, but when she was told that if her mistress was not produced forthwith, they would force a way in, she gave way. Mariella appeared in a revealing morning gown and, looking more curious than angry, asked what it was all about.

The *Préfet de Police*, played by an excellently made-up Pellicio, explained that Madame had entered the Principality of Monaco several times, despite having been expelled as an undesirable. 'We have been asked by the Monte Carlo police to arrest you,' he ended.

Mariella paled, she pleaded, she shouted, she wept. But the four men were adamant. She wanted to see a lawyer . . . and her Consul.

'There is not much anyone can do for you, Madame,' said

the '*Préfet*'. 'But as always in these cases we have asked your Consul to accompany us,' and bowed towards George, who for the sake of 25,000 francs had even sacrificed his Kaiser Wilhelm moustache. He was badly shaven, and looked tired and worn with red-rimmed eyes, after having driven from Monte through half the night; he wore a shabby suit and was a typical specimen of an underpaid Russian State employee. He bowed. 'Madame is Russian?' he said in Polish, of which he had a little knowledge. She answered in German. 'Yes, I am, but I do not speak the language very well.' That was all right with George, who did not either.

Mariella, left alone with George for a while, implored him to help. George said he was very eager to help such a beautiful lady, but what could he do? The best thing would be to depart at once and forget the whole thing. She did not like the idea, and George, privately, did not blame her.

'I will make it worth your while,' she said in the end, 'to have the *Préfet* forget everything and let me stay here.'

'It might cost you a lot of money for the *Préfet*,' said George, accepting a 1,000-franc note and slipping it in his pocket.

'How much?' she demanded.

George made a quick calculation. Provided Dimmi did not lose today, 50,000 francs would be sufficient to redeem the ring to which had to be added 25,000 francs for himself. Mariella looked appalled when she heard the figure. 'Then,' said George, 'it must be jail and expulsion!'

Madame paid 75,000 francs later in the afternoon. Pellicio, accompanied by a friend, arrived at the singer's suite with a closely written piece of paper. Mariella, already in a state of nervous breakdown, was forced to sign a confession that she had stolen by blackmail the sum of 82,000 francs, and promised never to tell what she knew. In return she could leave Nice by the next train.

'And do not go back on your word, Madame,' said Pellicio when he folded the signed document and put it into his pocket. 'This paper is good enough to ensure you a long stay in prison anywhere in Europe. I wish you a very good journey, Madame.'

Mariella left by the night train for Paris. A surprised Dimmi received George in his suite, gratefully accepted the 50,000 francs, and with Nikki left the next morning for Rome to redeem the ring. George with 25,000 additional francs in his pocket, paid his associates, dispatched Pellicio to send a tender telegram asking his lonely wife in the cold north of Europe to meet him at Munich's Four Seasons Hotel in a week's time, and departed the next morning for Zürich, Rorschach and then Lindau, built in Lake Constance.

*   *   *

(Four months later George was in Paris, when he received a visitor at his hotel. It was the Consul-General of Valebianco. He presented him with a personal letter from H.R.H. Prince Dimitrov, enclosing an official document. This said that in acknowledgement of services to the State of Valebianco and to the dynasty, he had been made a baron of the State, with the title: 'Baron d'Argente Viva' [Baron of Quick Money].

George showed it to Pellicio and laughed. 'Dimmi always had a funny sense of humour,' he said.)

Chapter 11

'I must buy a house,' said George to Pellicio as the small
excursion steamer entered Lindau harbour on the German
side of Lake Constance. He had promised his wife her own
home and the peaceful lakeside scenery seemed to him the
right setting for Prince Lahovary's married life.

'If you have to,' said Pellicio, 'then buy one. In other
words, you want to stop here?'

The local paper provided four addresses, the porter of
their hotel, the Bayrischer Hof, helpfully supplied a carriage
and they set out, as improbable a pair of house-hunters as
ever there was.

The largest of the four villas they visited took George's
fancy. A long, sprawling white house in the Bavarian style,
it stood in extensive grounds sloping down to the lake. It had
twelve rooms, with a huge kitchen in the basement and
servant's quarters in the lofts. From its windows there was a
glorious view of the snow-capped mountains on the Swiss
side, the lake and the steamers that plied between Switzerland and Germany. The dining-room led on to a stone terrace
and round the first storey ran a wooden balcony. The garden
was full of lilac bushes and at the end stood a small boat-
house on a private landing stage. The house was completely
furnished, mostly with big mahogany pieces; the pictures
on the walls were all of historic events and great German
battles. It belonged to an industrialist who had moved to the
north, and was very much a rich man's house. But then,
Prince Lahovary was a rich man. Or was he? A man with
unlimited resources, as long as there were fools enough about

to leave fortunes unguarded in hotel rooms, or as long as no epidemics killed off the neglected but gem-laden women. Besides, he had still more than 20,000 francs in his pocket. George bought the house as casually as other people buy a cake of soap, cash on the table that same afternoon, to the astonishment of the vendors who had expected long haggling over the 12,500 marks they demanded. His only condition was that all the papers should be ready for signature in the morning and that he should take possession of the villa at once.

Five days remained before George's meeting with his wife in Munich; in those five days the villa had to be prepared for her. An army of workers moved in from Lindau—carpenters, builders and plumbers, to repaint the rooms, modernize the kitchen, and install a bathroom instead of the tin tub in a small box-room half-way up the staircase. It was to be a enormous lapis lazuli bath, sunk into the floor of one of the bedrooms, which was to be tiled for that purpose. A carriage and pair were bought and a groom employed. But there was no stable, so one was erected within twenty-four hours. Pellicio, helped by the shrewd hotel porter, who was collecting a fortune in tips, engaged the household staff —an Austrian cook, a personal maid for Angelika, kitchen help from the nearby village of Schachen, housemaids and parlourmaids. And to lead them all, Frau Huber as house-keeper. Frau Huber, also an Austrian, was most highly recommended by the porter. She presented herself in the afternoon at the villa, arriving in a small carriage with all her belongings in a bulky straw trunk. She was about as tall as she was wide; she looked capable, energetic and about fifty years old. Her snow-white hair and rosy round face inspired confidence even though she talked non-stop in a local dialect that neither Pellicio nor George could completely understand. She had a big scrap-book into which were neatly glued letters of recommendation from former employers, among them a remarkable number of noble families; there was even a testimonial, with official stamp, from the Bavarian Royal Household in Munich, expressing the 'very best satisfaction' in the name of His Royal Highness, the Prince

Regent Leopold. What was good enough for the Bavarian Prince Regent was certainly approved by Prince Lahovary, and Frau Huber took command at once.

In the meantime Lindau was in an uproar. The sensational sale of the villa for cash was the main topic everywhere. The frantic efforts of the new owner to beautify the house, his lavish spending, made heads shake and tongues wag. But not for one moment was there any suspicion of George and his valet. When George appeared in town he was greeted politely by the locals who had decided to be proud of their new neighbour and accept him as a rich man who loved to squander his money harmlessly. The staff at the villa added to George's reputation as a genial millionaire. Wages higher than they had ever known before loosened their tongues in a constant pæan of praise for him. The plumbers and builders found him a true noble, a man who never checked the quantities of materials bought or asked to look at the accounts. They had been given five days to do the job and within three days the first floor was completely redecorated, the new bathroom nearing completion, and the lapis lazuli bath on its way from Zürich. With the assurance that the rest of the house would be ready when 'Frau Prinzessin' arrived, George left Pellicio in charge and went off to Munich.

Preceded by two page boys, carrying baskets full of spring flowers, he entered the ten-pounds-a-day suite reserved for him at the Hotel Vier Jahreszeiten, the feudal rendezvous of South Germany's highest nobility, to meet his wife. He stopped at the door and looked at her. She was simply dressed as he remembered her, and her eyes were laughing as she kissed him. She was obviously happy to see him back. Suddenly George found that her hair was not fluffy any longer, that her *coiffure* was more becoming than he remembered. Her hands and feet were still plump, but somehow quite shapely. She was desirable, wonderful, womanly. He felt more than mere sympathy for her. But while she had aroused his desire, her attitude had also changed. She seemed cooler, more reserved, even shy. When he discovered the reason he reacted characteristically, and recalled the event later: 'I had not married her for love and had much dreaded seeing Angelika again. Her love for me was embarrassing, although it was also a miracle. But now I felt suddenly that I loved her, wildly, passionately, with all my power. I wanted her . . . badly. I was certain that she was longing for me, but instead of responding to my fervent kisses, she smiled at me, thrust me gently back, and then whispered that she was expecting a baby.'

His baby! His child! George nearly went crazy with joy. He tore the flowers from the vases and showered them over Angelika. He rang the bell and ordered champagne, but told the waiter to bring a jug of milk as well! Tenderly he led Angelika to a chair and sat down at her feet, caressing her softly. George was *over*-considerate, he would get excited if she moved as much as a cushion or a book, or bent down to pick up something. He insisted on her going to a doctor to be certain that the birth of the child would not be endangered. He shouted at the hotel personnel if Angelika's wishes were not fulfilled at once, so that in the end she did not dare open her mouth. Sometimes he had visions of sinister men and women lurking in the dark to do harm to his unborn child. He told Angelika that he would take good care that the Koenigsbrueck clan would not succeed in their conspiracy against him. At night he sat in a corner of the darkened bedroom until Angelika fell asleep. He would suddenly rush out of the hotel to buy gifts for his wife: woollen scarves—despite the summer heat—gloves by the dozen pairs, flowers, baby linen. He wired Pellicio to secure the most expensive cradle he could find and to prepare the top-floor *salon* as a nursery. Then, to his horror he remembered . . . cash. He had left most of his money in Lindau and gone to Munich with only 1,000 marks. Now he was down to his last 100-mark note. He panicked. Against all his rules and principles he walked into the first room in his own hotel that he found open and took two pigskin suitcases. But in them were only clothes and in a fit of fury he threw the cases out of his window into the courtyard and at once went off again on a new raiding expedition. This time he succeeded in finding only a small diamond brooch and a ruby ring. Cursing the Germans for the drabness of their women, he rushed out of the hotel to sell his loot at the nearest jeweller for a petty 900 marks. It was just enough to pay the hotel bill, refund the hall porter for money laid out for presents for Angelika, and to buy tickets to Lindau. Long before the theft was discovered, Prince Lahovary and his wife were speeding by express train towards Lake Constance as, for the first time, he told her something of the villa near Lindau.

Angelika dearly loved George and she tried hard to get used to his eccentric behaviour and lavish spending, despite her natural instinct for economy and her life-long experience of austerity. She now tried to persuade herself that he would settle down in their 'little home' in South Germany and become an ideal family man.

Her arrival at Lindau however dazzled, and then horrified her. A flower-decked carriage with a uniformed groom stood in front of the station to drive them home. Outside the newly-painted villa, gleaming in the sun, stood four housemaids, two parlourmaids, all the kitchen staff, and the gardeners, waiting to welcome her. Pellicio, in a dark suit, kissed her hand, helped her out of the carriage, and presented a red-faced, perspiring Frau Huber in a black silk dress with lace cuffs.

That evening, on the terrace overlooking the lake, they dined while the last rays of the sun disappeared behind the mountains.

'George,' began Angelika, 'this is the most wonderful place I have ever seen in my life. It must have cost you a fortune! Can we afford it?'

At the best of times it was looking for trouble to ask George whether he could afford anything; now, with his finances at a very low level, it was disastrous. He jumped up, trembling with rage, and shouted: 'There is nothing a Lahovary cannot afford! Who do you think I am? Certainly not one of your fancy Guards officers, all in debt up to their necks!' As he saw her outraged expression he calmed down, adding quietly that he was well capable of managing his own affairs.

In the morning he regretted having spoiled their first

night in the new home and asked for forgiveness. Later
Pellicio brought him a Munich morning paper with the
report of a 'Mysterious theft in Luxury Hotel', and in the
best of moods and laughing happily he took his wife in the
carriage to the Lindau town hall and there at the Land
Registry transferred the entire property to her name—'As
a belated wedding gift and to make good my bad manners
last night.' His signature on the deed was erased by Angelika
and replaced by hers, sealed and counter-signed by the
town clerk.

His financial worries were very real. Much of the rebuild-
ing and repairs still had to be paid for, the wages of the staff
were soon due . . . and George had but a few hundred marks.
He announced that he had to attend an important director's
meeting in Paris but would be back in a week or so. When
Angelika, disappointed at being left alone again so soon,
broke into tears, he suggested she should invite her mother
to keep her company.

In Spa, in Belgium, first stop for Prince Lahovary and
Pellicio, George 'won' 4,000 francs at cards and wired half
to a Lindau bank for his wife. In Paris they took a suite in
the Hôtel de Londres in the rue Castiglione, George carefully
signing the register as George Mercadente. Surprisingly,
George seemed uninterested in Pellicio's intelligence reports
on possible pickings. He disappeared from the hotel for three
days with a little slip of a dancer he had met at the Café
Royal.

When at last he walked in, tired and red-eyed, to a
worried Pellicio he said: 'Well, she was a nice girl. First
pleasure and now business!' Even now he appeared to give
only half his attention and in the middle of their conversation
he jumped up, announced that he had to send a telegram to
his beloved wife, and ran down to the porter's desk. When
he returned, he declared that he would kill anybody who
dared to harm his wife and his unborn child. Pellicio said
later: 'He was worried about his health. There was nothing
wrong with his physical health, except for a tremendous
hangover from his amorous escapade, but he also seemed
to have lost his self-assurance, and was depressed about

money, which was quite unusual. He had the crazy idea that the child would starve.'

Pellicio told George about a 'job' in the Hotel St. James. George just nodded, and fell asleep. When he woke up he seemed to be his old debonair self, dressed with the greatest care, borrowed 1,000 francs from the hall porter, and sent another long and loving telegram to his wife, saying that he would return in a few days. Then he walked round to the Café Royal for another rendezvous with his little dancing girl. He did not return to his suite before late next morning, to be greeted by a cynically smiling Pellicio. He changed his clothes, and with a 'See you in the afternoon', walked the short distance to the Hotel St. James in the rue St. Honoré. It was now after lunch and the hotel was quiet. With a friendly nod, he passed the hall porter, took the lift to the third floor, and walked downstairs to the first floor and the rooms of the English lady Pellicio had spoken of so enthusiastically. The key was in the lock, and in the dressing-room he found, as he put it later, 'a load of jewels that made my heart jump with joy'. He blessed English women's fondness for jewels, so unlike the Germans.

He crammed the gems into his trouser pockets and moved to leave the room. Just then the door opened suddenly and a lady entered, to see George the minute she closed the door. He was leaning nonchalantly, quite at ease, against the window-sill and had a charming smile on his lips. 'What are you doing in my room?' she said sharply in English; then, with a glance at her dressing-table: 'Where are my jewels?'

George regarded her appraisingly. She was wearing an English tailor-made costume; her white hair under a tiny flower-decked hat emphasized the healthy, rosy complexion of her face. She carried a diminutive handbag and a sunshade, and George guessed her age as fifty or fifty-five. He did not move from the window-sill, even as she approached swinging the sunshade menacingly. When she was only a few feet away, he said in his best English: 'Madame, this is very dangerous,' pointing at the whirling sunshade. 'You might damage one of the mirrors, or even knock down a vase, which, I believe, are genuine Sèvres and rather expensive. *What* did you say about your jewels?'

The lady stopped, speechless, and dropped her sunshade. George bent and picked it up and put it on a settee. 'Who are you?' she asked more quietly. 'What have you done with my gems?' As he did not answer, she went on: *'You* have stolen them!'

George shook his head disapprovingly. *'So* many questions, Madame,' he said. 'And impolite questions at that! You allege I have stolen your jewels? But you have no proof. Neither have I any proof that you had any jewels at all! Do you wish me to ring the bell and call for assistance?'

On the lady's face appeared the suspicion of a smile. She sat down in an easy chair. She was a London authoress of detective stories who had been invited to Paris by the British Embassy. This situation was very much to her liking, if one did not consider the missing gems. She was not sure what to do and George sensed her indecision.

'I am awfully sorry about your jewels,' he said, 'but I am certain they must be somewhere. I do hope you have insured them? I do not really know what I could do to help you.' He bowed slightly. 'No hard feelings on my part, Madame!'

He adjusted his bowler hat to the right angle, bowed again and added: 'Do not do anything foolish, please, before I have left the hotel.'

He marched to the door, opened it and walked out into the corridor. As he closed the door softly behind him, he had a last glimpse of the lady rising from her chair and walking to the telephone. He raced down the stairs but sauntered through the hall past a politely bowing hall porter who was just about to answer a furiously ringing telephone. Within a minute he had disappeared round the corner and was among the dense crowds of the rue St. Honoré.

A carriage brought him to the Hôtel du Louvre, opposite the Palais Royal, where, he remembered, Pellicio reported a very careless Dutch family from the Colonies residing in rooms nos. 204 and 205. But these rooms were locked. However, a chambermaid obligingly opened a door for him, when he said he had left his key inside. Alas, inside were only a few small gold articles and a ruby bangle, so he returned to his waiting carriage and drove to the Bastille to pay a call on Machinelle. At four in the afternoon he was back in the Hôtel de Londres with 35,000 francs in his pocket. His first words to Pellicio were: 'Go and get me a pistol!'

'What for?' Pellicio asked, with horror. 'I always thought you hated violence. Do you want to start a war?'

For the first time in their long relationship George became furiously angry with Pellicio. 'I do not like being questioned,' he shouted, throwing a bundle of banknotes into the valet's face. 'You are impertinent and a discouraging pessimist! You hamper my style! You try to control my life . . . you are getting too big for your breeches!' But a minute later he was his old self again, and his rage completely forgotten. He produced a bottle of cognac and drank with Pellicio, explaining to him that he wanted the pistol to shoot the doctor in Lindau if he proved to have neglected his pregnant wife!

They saw the Paris evening papers in Strasbourg next morning, with 'Jewel Mystery in Grand Hotel' splashed across the front pages. There was a satisfied smirk on George's face and some ironic clapping from Pellicio. When the train was about to leave for the other side of the Rhine, Pellicio looked at George thoughtfully and said suddenly: 'I am not travelling to Lindau with you.'

Surprised, hurt, George at once apologized to Pellicio for his outburst of the previous day.

'It is not that,' replied Pellicio. 'I do not want to be a burden. Your wife does not approve of me. Neither does your noble mother-in-law, and as you know, I hate the Boche. Look what they have done to our beautiful Alsace Lorraine! Besides, you are a family man now, George, and you do not need me so much. I can be more useful to you in Paris.'

'I am always at your disposal, George,' were Pellicio's parting words. 'But I hope for your sake you will not need me again.' He meant it sincerely, for in his romantic, southern heart he was extremely fond of George, as well as grateful for the fortune lying in his name at the Credit Lyonnais in Paris.

'Again I cursed my uncontrollable temper,' recalled George later, 'and was really sorry about Pellicio's decision.' They shook hands and George continued his journey alone, except for twelve suitcases and trunks and a score of parcels containing hurriedly bought presents for Angelika.

George arrived in Lindau on July 18, 1899, to meet a deliriously happy wife and a hard-faced mother-in-law (although she *was* a little pleased that he returned without Pellicio). George's first thoughts were for his unborn child, and he declared that in the morning he would drive to the *Standesamt* (Registrar's Office) in Lindau to register their marriage according to German law and legalize the birth of the child.

The four weeks that George remained in the villa were not pleasant. He was by German standards a man of substance; he could have invested his money or started a business, but to work never occurred to him. The cash burned in his pockets and he felt cramped and uneasy because he could not spend it freely. There were endless quarrels and arguments with his mother-in-law, who did nothing to hide her distrust of George. He spent much of his time at a wine hall in Lindau, where he met a striking Italian girl, the sister of a fruit seller in the town market. Under the pretext of business, he travelled to Munich—but with the Italian girl—returning a week later with a load of nursery equipment. His mother-in-law stopped him in the morning-room after his return and told him bluntly: 'I detest you!' She knew all about his escapade in Munich!

George laughed in her face and banged his fist on a table. 'I *need* women,' he said maliciously, 'beautiful women. I need them . . . as you need another face! In the state my wife is in, I cannot endanger the birth of my child by confining my . . . er . . . activities to her!'

Baroness von Koenigsbrueck's answer was just as blunt. She threatened to bring Angelika's brother to Lindau to horsewhip such a scoundrel of a husband and then take his sister home. George pulled out his little pistol (which was unloaded) and asserted that he would shoot the Baron down like a mad dog.

It was now open war. Koenigsbruecks *v*. Lahovary, with mother-in-law publicly proclaiming that George was a crook and a mountebank. No one, neither her mother nor her husband, had the slightest consideration for Angelika, who had locked herself in her rooms, seeing nobody but a sympathetic Frau Huber.

George left the villa on Lake Constance exactly six weeks after his arrival, without even saying farewell to his wife, for he was now convinced that *she* was conspiring with her family against him. He put 25,000 marks in Angelika's bank account, and meeting Pellicio at Baden Baden, said sadly: 'How I regret having married that Baroness Angelika—such great idiocy!'

Prince Lahovary and valet returned at once to the circuit of the great international hotels—Baur au Lac in Zürich; Hôtel des Anglais in Nice; Hôtel de Paris in Monte— gambling with varying success and stealing until, with 60,000 francs, they arrived back at the Hotel Continental in Paris. Occasionally, between gambling, love-making and robbing lonely women, George had brief thoughts of his wife in Lindau and of the expected child, and Pellicio was sent regularly to telegraph affectionate messages to the villa, but with no apologies for the flight.

On the evening of September 18, 1899, an urgent telephone message from Pellicio reached George at a gambling casino in the rue Royale. A telegram had announced the birth of a daughter at the villa on Lake Constance. Stuffing banknotes and gold coins in his pocket, George raced back to the hotel to order their departure for Germany next morning. There was still time to buy presents for his wife in a whirlwind shopping spree along the rue Rivoli and rue de la Paix: silk gowns and *two* gold watches, a diamond ring, a dozen hats, blouses, shawls, perfume and a crate of champagne. For his daughter it had to be something very special, a gift worthy of a Princess Lahovary. Since it was now after shopclosing hours, he dragged the coach-builder Gigon from his suburban home in Clignancourt into his carriage, bribed him to reopen his premises and bought a dog cart and then a brown pony from a stable in St. Lazare. This extraordinary present for a newborn baby was rushed to the Gare de l'Est and loaded on a freight wagon to be attached to the express in the morning. A hurriedly summoned groom agreed to travel with the pony as far as the border. George returned to his hotel with just enough time for breakfast before leaving for the station once more. He was gay, joking with Pellicio, even though his money was now down to 1,000 francs. He counted the hours until he could see the child.

When George was installed in his reserved compartment, Pellicio again declined to return to the villa. For probably the first time in all his travels, George made an honest declaration of his luggage, to the German customs officials in Metz, and to his surprise had no difficulties when he told them that he was on the way to see his newborn child. They even let the pony go through, and promised to warn Strasbourg, Freiburg and other stations on the way to provide it with water and feed.

George arrived in Lindau late at night. There was no one to meet him. There were difficulties with the pony, which could not be unloaded until the morning. George left his luggage at the station, had the dog-cart unloaded, put himself in front of it, and pulled it through the empty streets, out of town to the villa on the lake.

He was still in high spirits, but when he found the house in darkness and it took a quarter of an hour for a servant to answer his knocking and shouting, he was convinced that his mother-in-law had arranged this cold reception—and was wild with rage when she herself came to the door.

Seeing George standing beside a small vehicle, she shouted: 'What do you want?' George did not answer, but pushed past her, raced up the stairs and into his wife's bedroom, closely followed by an outraged Baroness. Angelika in bed whispered: 'George . . .' and fainted. George, however, was concerned first with the child in the cradle next to her mother's bed. He wanted to take the little bundle in his arms, but was roughly pushed back by his mother-in-law.

Frau Huber rolled into the room to tend to Angelika, George raved at the Baroness in all the languages he knew. But the old lady was not subdued. Acidly she said: 'You can look at your child the moment you give me the documents concerning your Romanian family, not one second before!' Firmly she planted herself in front of the cradle.

George gripped her by the arm. 'Go away!' he shouted. 'Leave this house at once, or I'll call the police.'

'That suits me perfectly,' she retorted. '*I* should have thought of that earlier. A fine nobleman *you* are. You are a crook, my friend, and I am not so sure that is not how you get all the money you squander!'

Just then Angelika opened her eyes. 'Do not quarrel,' she whimpered and the baby, now fully awake, burst into loud crying. George felt helpless, he knelt down by his wife's bed and kissed her hand until she calmed down. Then, persuaded by the efficient Frau Huber, he went down for a restless sleep in a drawing-room chair.

During the ten days he stayed at the villa he spent most of his time with the baby. Angelika he regarded as a participant in the plot against him. When one morning he overheard his mother-in-law telling her daughter that her husband must be a crook, and that the only thing to do was to notify the police, he could stand the position no longer, even though Angelika's answer showed that she stood by her husband and still loved him. The old Baroness was getting dangerous and George decided to go away for ever. Without saying good-bye to his wife or daughter, he drove to the station in a luggage-crammed carriage, but was back an hour later to fetch his dog—'I cannot leave the poor beast in this prison-like atmosphere.'

He boarded the steamer for Switzerland without a single thought of the villa, where he had once believed he would find peace and happiness.

He travelled to his favourite Lucerne and took rooms in the Hotel Viktoria. This time under the name of Manolesco. Now there was only one thing of interest for George: *Money*. He decided to sell his dog for 'working capital' and embarked on a reconnaissance of some of the big lakeside hotels. At the Schweizerhof he found an unlocked room on the first floor and picked up two diamond rings, two diamond brooches and cash, totalling 35,000 francs, belonging to a high official of the Belgian Government. While George was thus engaged, the commissionaire of the same hotel paraded up and down in front of the building with the valuable borzoi dog until he sold it for 200 francs. Financially safe for the first time in weeks, George felt himself again, all his audacity and cunning restored. He travelled to Baden Baden and sold some of the gems in a jeweller's shop, having previously telephoned the owner that he had lost at the tables and was forced to part with his family heirlooms.

On the way to Frankfurt he picked up in the train a 'quite acceptable buxom young lady', and as 'Dr. Davila and wife' took an inexpensive suite in the Palace Hotel, Fürstenhof.

He had not been in serious trouble with the police for a long time, and therefore felt thoroughly secure, certain that scarcely anything was known about him. He was almost right. His various alibis were unknown to the police in general for, as George knew very well, normally the forces of different countries did not bother much to exchange information on wanted men. He had, however, not counted on the special efficiency of the Swiss and German police. The Swiss authorities in Lucerne, waging a campaign against hotel thieves who ruined the reputation of their greatest industry—tourism—had invented a system of describing all robberies in a daily printed circular sent to all big towns, holiday resorts and spas of Switzerland and a certain distance into Germany. One such circular reached the police in Baden Baden a few days after George's theft, and the sale of some of the stolen articles was discovered at the jeweller's, who produced a signed form from the vendor, stating they were his property, as German law demanded. The Baden Baden police photographed this form and also sent the picture to Frankfurt. There, an ambitious Prussian policeman on his daily routine check through hotel registers noticed some similarity between the jewellery-form signature and that on the registration slip of a Dr. Davila. George's room was searched while he was out and one of the Lucerne brooches was found. He was arrested and jailed pending extradition to Switzerland.

Meanwhile the police found out that George Manolesco had a wife in Lindau and immediately notified her of the situation. George, anticipating just this, had already written to her explaining that in his 'idiotic desire to help a friend' he had been jailed for a theft committed by a certain Georges Popesko who had asked him to sell the gems. 'Until my innocence is proved I have no money, so please send me twenty marks. I embrace you, my darling, and hope you and the child are well. Are you fully recovered? Give my love to Frau Huber, and I suggest we christen our baby Jeanne, which is a wonderful name.' A worried Angelika arrived in Frankfurt barely a fortnight after the birth of the baby to see her husband in jail. He insisted that it was all a mistake, and she left him with the twenty marks.

When George learned that Angelika was to visit him, he had made up his mind to fake insanity. He started singing and dancing in his cell, talking to imaginary visitors, brooding, shouting and demanding impossible things from the guards. The Frankfurt police psychiatrist, however, decided that he was perfectly normal, extradition was granted and he was taken by two policemen to jail in Lucerne.

During the four weeks' interrogation he continued to feign madness. Daily he delivered long diatribes against the 'bad service' in jail. He criticized the lack of comfort, the hard bed. He used the prison guards as messengers and valets, ordering them to press his trousers, to fetch him papers from the kiosk at the station. He had reached Frankfurt with twenty-one suits of clothes and numberless silk shirts and patent-leather shoes packed in eleven cases; and since his valet was not available, it was the duty of the warders to keep things in shape! If the warders protested, he became abusive, threatening to report them and screaming that they were not dealing with a Swiss yokel, but with a gentleman of standing, a man of the world.

In March 1900, the public prosecutor of the Canton Lucerne, Herr Müller, demanded two and a half years' penal servitude for George. The defending lawyer, Dr. Oswald, maintained that it was only a minor theft, and that in any event the accused could not be held responsible for his actions. He asked for a reduction to four months' detention so that the prisoner could soon return to his family, adding: 'Only his unhappy family life has made him a thief.'

The jury found George Manolesco guilty of theft, but considered that he was not fully responsible for his actions. He was sent to prison for six months, and banned from entering Switzerland for ten years after his release. Two months of detention before the trial was to be deducted from the jail term.

George, who had dressed most carefully for his trial, stood motionless in the dock when the judgment was announced. When the presiding judge had finished, he stroked his Kaiser Wilhelm moustache, bowed politely to the jury and to the judges, and in a voice with just the right suggestion of remorse, thanked the court for its fair and just treatment. Then he crossed himself three times, and as the warders took him towards the cells, he turned in the door and bowed again to all corners of the court before leaving.

Chapter 12

It was at the end of July 1900, two months after George's twenty-ninth birthday, that two taciturn policemen escorted him from Lucerne to Basle and the French border. His lordly wardrobe had shrunk to one case containing only his very best suits and he had a little money from the sale of his other belongings. He arrived in Paris on August 1, and took a room in a cheap hotel on the Left Bank, in the rue Monsieur-le-Prince, under the name of George Mercadente. At once he took the railway to Charenton, a respectable middle-class suburb in the south, between the River Seine and the Bois de Vincennes, in search of Franzesco Auguste Pellicio, ex-valet and confidant, now in retirement.

Pellicio had a bungalow of grey sandstone with a red roof and a small veranda holding two rocking-chairs facing each other. The small front lawn was dotted with statues of dwarfs and fairy-tale animals. It was a well-kept house, differing little from any other in the road, where small businessmen and retired shop-keepers lived on whatever capital they had saved in a lifetime of hard work. George remembered that Pellicio was actually a rich man with a banking account whose interest would have allowed him to live in a fashionable suburb without worries. But Pellicio was always cautious.

His knock at the door was answered by the Corsican himself, wearing gardening clothes, a trowel in hand. For a second or two he stared at the caller as if he had seen a ghost. Then the trowel clattered on the tiled floor and a great smile grew on his face. 'George!' he cried, embracing him. 'Come in, come in! I am very glad to see you back.'

George followed Pellicio into the front room. 'I will just get my jacket,' said Pellicio and left his guest sitting on a purple plush sofa. It was a formal room, very tidy and obviously only used on great occasions. The window blinds were half down so that the sunlight would not fade the furnishings. On the narrow mantelpiece stood small porcelain figures, a silver bell, and two candlesticks. The sideboard held a glass bowl of artificial fruits. On the two side walls hung gilt-framed oil paintings, one a hunting scene, the other a mountain landscape. In the centre of the room was a massive circular oak dining-table, highly polished, with a crochetted centrepiece on which stood another glass bowl, of roses. Around the table were high-backed leather chairs arranged in painstaking order. In corners stood an aspidistra and a palm tree in iron pots. A paraffin lamp hung from the ceiling exactly over the middle of the table. It was the type of room one would expect to find here, and George was disappointed.

Pellicio returned, now wearing his blue serge suit with collar and tie, and carrying a bottle and two glasses. 'Well,' said George. 'I see you have settled down for good.' His voice had a slightly ironical undertone. 'And you are doing yourself proud.' He nodded, looking around the room again. 'I also discover the feminine touch.'

'Certainly,' said Pellicio, not in the slightest offended by the unspoken disapproval of his friend and former master. 'You will meet Lorette later, when she comes back from the shops,' and with a sweeping gesture of both hands, embracing the entire room, he added, 'I always have wondered what you would say if you came along. I know it is a bit different from the Hotel Continental, I give you that, but believe me, it is very comfortable and homely.' He poured two glasses of brandy. 'Even *if* you do not approve.'

George protested. 'But I do approve,' he said. 'Very much so. And I do like it too. It seems to be a very well-kept place, and does you credit. And who is Lorette?'

'She is a very nice girl,' Pellicio answered seriously. 'I met her at a dance. When I bought this place, she agreed to move in with me. She is only twenty and keeps the house excellently.'

'And what have you told her?' asked George.

'Nothing. She thinks I have retired, and so I have.'

'Enjoying it?'

'Well . . . yes,' replied Pellicio and sipped his drink. 'It is a nice, quiet life,' he said grinning. 'No excitement at all apart from discussing once or twice a week the thrills of fishing with the neighbours in the 'Colombine d'Or' at the corner. Sometimes I think it a little too peaceful and wish something would happen. But drink your cognac, George. It is a genuine Tricoche 1885, I hope you will appreciate it.'

George sipped his cognac and agreed it was excellent. 'And what about Lorette?' he asked. 'What would she say if you went away in search for . . . ahem . . . excitement?'

Pellicio grinned. 'Most probably she would weep a bit. And then she would curse you, George. But what about your family?'

'Do not remind me of the Koenigsbruecks,' said George, with a dry laugh. 'They do not know me any more. Angelika has returned to Saxonia, to her brother's farm. She has my blessing. The bailiff has been in the house, and they are selling it now. That's all I know. My little Jeanette, God bless her . . . she probably one day will be a country bumpkin like the rest of the family. She is nearly a year old now. I must not forget to send her a splendid birthday present. But the family . . . I told you they wouldn't make any trouble, they are much too afraid of scandal. One *should not* marry, and if one must then certainly not a house-broken girl with an aristocratic family and nothing else behind her.'

By the time Lorette returned from the shops Pellicio and George had come to an understanding. The valet would take up his duties again with George and make another looting trip.

'I have to get into shape again,' said George, 'and the earlier we begin the better it is. I am quite penniless.'

As predicted, Lorette wept a bit when she heard the news, but she did not curse George. She was very much in love with Pellicio and proud that his old master wanted him back in service. When Pelicio emphasized that this was not the end of their love affair, she was quite happy. 'You stay here,' he said to her. 'When I return, we will marry.'

They had chosen to start in Deauville, now in full season. Then something happened which made George change his plans.

He had, for the first time in his career, *too good* a Press! The story of the gentleman-thief who regarded the jail as a hotel and was not satisfied with the service, who behaved like a lord, who treated judges and jury so courteously, had been widely reported. The fact that the thief was a member of a noble family, whose name had been kept secret by the court, had only added to the value of the story. 'George Manolesco' had become unenviably famous. One journalist called him the 'Prince of Thieves', and in a very colourful article credited him with countless crimes of which he was quite innocent.

George always enjoyed reading about himself, and was proud of the title 'Prince of Thieves'. But he was angry at the incorrect list of robberies. 'They accuse me of every petty job in any hotel during the last ten years,' he said disgusted. 'Who do they think I am? Here . . .' slapping his fist on a newspaper cutting '. . . a pair of ear-rings in Nantes. Idiots! I don't bother with trifles, and besides I have never in my life been in Nantes.' His vanity hurt, he made up his mind to correct this picture of himself.

'Aren't you already notorious enough?' warned Pellicio. 'After this,' and he pointed at the newspaper cutting, 'the police will be after you as never before.'

George shrugged. 'That's what they are paid for. They have been looking for me for more than ten years and only caught me twice. The police are fools, and will be looking for Monsieur George Manolesco. Monsieur George Manolesco will arrange some proper publicity, and then—to hell with George Manolesco! It has never occurred to them to look for Prince Lahovary. Well, I *am* Prince Lahovary, and I strongly resent that Monsieur Manolesco is being accused of petty theft!'

Pellicio was sent to town to deliver a letter to the offending journalist, inviting him to meet Monsieur George

Manolesco. 'I will be driving along the Allée de Longchamps in the Bois de Boulogne in a closed carriage and then around the Cercle du Bois de Boulogne,' wrote George. 'I will pick you up at the Cercle at six o'clock in the evening where the riding path crosses in the direction of the Porte Maillot. But I warn you to come alone without any companion, and certainly without the police, or there will be no story for you.'

Enjoying the cloak-and-dagger atmosphere of the meeting, George drove around the circle four times to make absolutely certain the journalist was alone.

Three days later an article appeared about George Manolesco's adventures as the 'Prince of Thieves'. He had protested energetically against being accused of every theft the police could not solve. 'The police can never solve any mystery,' he was quoted as saying. 'Ten years ago they caught me by my own carelessness and only by accident, when I visited a jeweller and 'borrowed' some pearls. They will never catch me again. And if they do, they cannot hold me. The few months in Lucerne—that was a very foolish thing. But if they could find witnesses for all the necklaces I have taken up to now, I would probably spend the rest of my life in prison. Which I would definitely not like. But all my victims, if you must call them that, make little trouble. That is why I pick on them. *I would never rob anybody who could not afford it.* And if I do so, by accident, I return their property to them.' The article recounted the story of the blind girl in Rome.

'It is not worth while stealing from poor people,' George continued, 'not even from well-off people, who are free to raise hell. As a matter of fact it pays to steal only from ambassadors and above!'

Not a word could the journalist extract from George about his marriage and his family.

The new article pictured Manolesco as an arch-scoundrel, but with his own code of honour. The public now took a strong liking for his bravado, the police were furious, and George's underworld network reported that orders had been issued to catch him at all costs. Clearly it would be stupidly risky to stay in France, and he could not go to Switzerland. He chose the north of Germany as battlefield and took the train to Baden Baden without any trouble from the authorities, who were looking for him elsewhere. A few days in Baden Baden secured him 4,000 marks and he went on to Berlin, which was fresh territory to him. Pellicio followed very reluctantly—he hated travelling into the heart of 'Boche-land', but he was consoled to find Berlin a lively city with broad avenues, beautiful girls, good restaurants, and a hotel which even the critical valet could only consider 'excellently kept'. They booked in at the Kaiserhof, to sleep under the same roof as ambassadors and courtiers, grand dukes and industrialists. Pellicio still objected to the strutting, military bearing of all males between fifteen and seventy, their love of uniform and titles, and the eternal heel-clicking.

*　　*　　*

After five days in the Kaiserhof, dining at Hiller's Restaurant on the Unter den Linden, and adventures by night with accommodating ladies of the notorious Café Bauer, George needed money once again.

His first victim in Berlin he found in the illustrious person of the Grand Duke of Oldenburg, who had a suite in the Hotel Continental near the Friedrichstrasse Station. Walking in the street, George had met Herr Ignaz Skamperl, alias Prince Nicotin, who greeted him effusively, much to George's disgust; he did not like the loud Hungarian enthusiasm. Skamperl, who looked even more yellow-faced than George could remember from Frankfurt, was on the bill of the Reichshallen Variety Theatre, and hoped to see George and Pellicio after the performance. Despite his dislike, George regarded the meeting with the artist as a good omen, and continued his walk to the hotel of the Grand Duke.

The doorman lifted his cap to the distinguished visitor, and George went straight to the reception desk in the palm-studded hall and asked for the room number of his intended victim. He took the lift to the second floor, where a chamber-maid opened the Grand Duke's rooms for him, generously tipped by the 'awfully nice gentleman'. He entered and left the door ajar.

Just at that moment, however, the Grand Duke's footman came along the corridor to see with surprise that the door of his master's suite was not properly closed. As he entered, he found a gentleman standing over the Grand Duchess's dressing-table. 'What are you doing here?' he asked.

George turned slowly round with an affable smile. 'Ah, my good man,' he said. 'I am looking for the Grand Duke. Would you tell him that Prince George of Saxonia wishes to see him at one o'clock.' He took a visiting card from his pocket, flashed it in front of the eyes of the servant, to show the embossed crown, and walked to the door. 'Do not forget to convey my message,' he said, closing the door behind him.

The result of that morning's work was not satisfactory so far; due to the interruption he had found only a couple of hundred marks. But as he passed the porter's desk, he heard a page being instructed to go to the restaurant and reserve a table for His Excellency, Monsieur Nitoff of no. 361. When George had studied the morning papers he had found in the daily list of prominent visitors to the German capital that Monsieur Nitoff, *en route* for Paris, was adjutant to the Russian Tsar, and thus well worth attention. At 2 p.m. he therefore returned to the Hotel Continental and walked straight up to room 361. This time the key was in the lock. To be on the safe side, he knocked at the door and as he received no answer, entered. On a little side-table in Madame's boudoir he found a pearl necklace and a few minutes later he was out of the hotel.

Cash was still rather short. 'You cannot pay with pearls,' said Pellicio, who suggested they should move from the expensive Kaiserhof into a smaller hotel. They chose the Stadt London, and in the evening went to the Reichshallen Theatre to see Prince Nicotin. After the show they went with him to his lodgings in an artist's boarding-house, Eber, in the Jaegerstrasse, to discuss business. An enthusiastic

Skamperl promised to get rid of the pearls at a good price, and even paid 2,000 marks on account, which was very much to George's liking.

The next morning the papers were full of the theft. It was stated that the vanished necklace was worth 40,000 marks. The police declared that they had a clue already. The doorman, Bellgardi, had observed a well-dressed gentleman enter the hotel twice in quick succession and leave in a hurry. He had not even given him a tip. The Grand Duke's footman confirmed the doorman's description as the same as that of the stranger he had surprised in his master's rooms.

Skamperl arrived at the Hotel Stadt London in the early afternoon with a grave face. 'Your description in the papers is very good,' he said to George, and Pellicio shook his head disapprovingly at the carelessness of his master. 'They will check all hotels,' said Skamperl worried. 'The Berlin police are very thorough.'

They decided to accept his offer to transfer to his boarding-house. 'They are not so particular there about signing registers and arrival forms.'

On the way to the Jaegerstrasse, they passed the Hotel Bristol, on Unter den Linden, and George asked the coachman of the *Droschke* to stop and wait a few minutes. He entered the hotel and paid a flying visit to number three on his list of victims, the newly arrived Mexican Minister, Señor Gallardo, to whose rooms he was directed by a well-tipped page boy. Seven minutes later he returned to the coach, smiling contentedly at Pellicio and Skamperl, and with a huge diamond-studded star in his pocket and a large platinum picture-frame under his coat.

'While we are at it,' he said in the best of humour as the carriage passed the Hotel Kaiserhof, 'I might as well go on with a good day's work.' While the coachman waited with a fidgeting Pellicio and a frightened Skamperl in the back, George walked up the marble stairs to the rooms of a wealthy Junker whose acquaintance he had made in the hotel a few days earlier, and who was visiting the capital for the Christmas and New Year celebrations. Here, in five minutes, he found gems worth about 8,000 marks.

During the newspaper uproar that followed this latest series of thefts, George and Pellicio stayed out of sight. When the storm abated a little George decided to sell some of the gems himself and leave the rest with Pellicio and Skamperl to handle. He took the night train to Dresden and sold some gems to a Court jeweller, explaining once more that misfortune at the card tables had forced him to part with the family heirlooms. He took a room in the Hotel Europaeischer Hof, undecided what to do next. Should he return to Berlin or was it safer to stay away? His mind was made up for him when in the hall of the hotel he suddenly found himself face to face with his brother-in-law.

Recognition was mutual. Before George could evade him, the Baron gripped him by the arm, shook him violently, and then slapped him twice, right and left across the face. For a fraction of a second George was wordless. Then he found his wits again, pushed aside the horrified hall porter and with great dignity said calmly: 'Under normal circumstances I should now send you my seconds for offending the honour of Prince Lahovary. But I do not fight lunatics and rogues—only gentlemen!'

Now it was the turn of the Royal Saxonian Captain and Escort Chief in the Guards Regiment, Baron Ernst Georg August von Koenigsbrueck, to be at a loss for words, as George laughed in his scarlet face. Turning to the hall porter and smiling round at the cluster of guests, George said: 'Take him away, porter, before he becomes dangerous. Accompany him to his room. Usually he is quite harmless! I will telephone the institution he is in and they will come and fetch him.'

He walked round the Baron, who was still incoherent with rage, and left the hotel. He was furious himself, and to calm himself decided to go to the near-by station for a coffee. There he had a second shock. Big headlines in the morning papers disclosed that Skamperl had been arrested and that jewels had been found on him. George read that investigations had unearthed several visits by Skamperl to a certain Prince Lahovary in a Berlin hotel. Both the French valet, Pellicio, and Prince Lahovary had disappeared. Moreover, the description of the Prince was also that of the notorious George Manolesco.

Now *all* was known.

George raced to the ticket counter to buy himself a ticket for Austria. By now they would have seen the papers at his hotel, so he did not dare return there for his luggage. He went into the station restaurant and simply took a coat from a hanger, picked up a small suitcase, and boarded his train. It was one hour to the border and he had no difficulty in crossing, to reach Prague, the capital of Bohemia, in the evening. The next day he sold the rest of the jewels in Prague.

Germany and Austria were now too dangerous for him, Switzerland was barred, and he decided to go to Italy.

He arrived in Genoa in January 1901, with new luggage and some money, and booked in at the Grand Hôtel de Génes near the Teatro Carlo Felice, as George Mercadente. When his money was nearing its end he began his hotel thefts again, acquired a diamond brooch from a Spanish lady which brought 4,000 francs from Carcola when he visited him on a day-excursion trip by steamer. But his enterprises in Genoa lacked drive. George was worried about the Berlin affair, about Pellicio, and about losing the money due to him from Skamperl for the sale of part of the robberies.

In the meantime the Berlin police had circulated George's description to all police forces in Europe, and it was not long before the Italian authorities became suspicious of the stranger at the Hôtel de Génes and checked up on him. George did not realize that times had changed. George was visited by two detectives in his room, asked to come with them to the *Questura*, and there arrested and put in jail; and the Berlin police were told of the catch by proud Italians.

He was collected from the police jail in Genoa by two German *Kriminalkommissare* and taken, handcuffed to one of his guards, to Berlin's *Kriminal Gericht* at Moabit. He appeared before his judges on May 26, 1902, in Berlin, for one of the most amusing and sensational trials of the new century.

To George's surprise the Berlin police were extremely

well informed about many of his enterprises, and he decided to admit a great number of his thefts. Having been informed by his advocate, the famous criminal lawyer Dr. Schwindt, that Pellicio had succeeded in returning to France, and was out of reach of the Prussian police, there was no need to be too careful. The charges against Manolesco and Skamperl were of theft, and George felt it was only due to Skamperl's carelessness that the whole thing had come to light. He turned again to his old trick of pretending insanity.

Half a dozen psychiatrists, led by the world-famous Professor Koeppen, examined him. Their opinions differed widely.

During one examination by Professor Koeppen, the psychiatrist asked: 'Your name is George Manolesco?'

'No,' said George haughtily. 'It is Prince Lahovary.'

'And what is your profession?'

'Millionaire.'

'I see,' nodded the professor. 'Have you any documents to prove that?'

'Sir!' shouted George jumping up furiously, 'my illustrious and noble person is enough to prove my title.'

The question of the name came up at once in the trial. 'You married in Genoa,' said the judge. 'Under what name?'

'Prince Lahovary,' answered George proudly. 'The Archbishop of Genoa in person married me.'

'How did you get that title?'

'It belongs to me,' answered George. 'Since 1106, all my ancestors called themselves Lahovary. It is an old and famous name.'

The President of the Court nodded. 'We know that the Lahovarys are an old family. Why does your father not use the name?'

'Simple, Herr President. He does not like it. Probably he likes the title of a captain better.'

'And you have not stolen documents of identity from a Prince Lahovary?'

'NO!' shouted George furiously. 'I have not. I do not steal!'

'What about the theft at a Lucerne hotel? Where you stole valuables worth twenty thousand francs?'

'I *took* them! But they were from rich people.'

The President shook his head in despair. 'So, you believe you are allowed to steal?' he asked. 'Is it permitted in Romania to enter the house of Prince Lahovary to steal gems?'

George thought that over for a few minutes. 'I do not think that this would be in order,' he said finally.

Later it came to the question of irresponsibility and sanity. The President asked Manolesco: 'Your mother has been in an asylum?'

'Yes,' answered George, with tears in his eyes. 'My beloved mother. She was mad!' and he added that his brother, too, had been insane (he had never had a brother). 'I am crazy, too!' he shouted jubilantly. 'Our entire family is crazy, including my father. But they did not want me to be put in a mad-house, for I am the only son.'

'And you believe that robbery is allowed?'

'It is not robbery, Herr President. If I see things lying around and I like them, I just take them!' And taking the judge's gold pencil from his desk and putting it into his own pocket, he added: 'Just as I take this pencil. It is quite simple. I enter a room. I find things. I take the things, and I go . . . good-bye . . .!'

But he put the gold pencil back on the judge's bench.

'Why do you do it?' asked the President.

George shrugged. 'If people are rich, it does not really matter to them. And why should I, Prince Lahovary, drink beer at Christmas while everybody else drinks champagne?'

'Your views,' said the President drily, 'are rather unconventional.'

While George gave the performance of his life, his advocate, Dr. Schwindt, used all his talents to *prove George guilty*. For he knew that if his client were found guilty he would go to prison for two or three years; but if found insane, it would mean committal for life to an asylum. Dr. Schwindt pleaded guilty.

On May 28, 1902, the court pronounced its judgment, clearly under the strong influence of the Koenigsbrueck family who had mobilized all their resources to ensure that their name would be played down as much as possible. To them, a George who would be free again in a few years time was a Sword of Damocles over their heads. He had to be put away once and for all. George Manolesco, alias Prince Lahovary, was pronounced not guilty, because he was suffering from hallucinations and delusions of grandeur. The court ordered him to be freed immediately, to be given into the custody of medical specialists, and to be sent to the Prussian State Asylum at Dalldorf near Berlin.

It was now very difficult to prove Skamperl's guilt, only his connection with George . . . and George was not guilty. As there had to be one scapegoat, he was held until evidence of an old theft was secured, and Skamperl disappeared into oblivion.

On May 31, 1902, George was locked in an observation cell of the forbidding redstone establishment at Dalldorf. Now he proved a model patient. He was good natured, polite, sweet tempered. He was a favourite with doctors and the husky male nurses. He never complained. He insisted only that his heavy drill institution suit should be pressed every day!

Next George learned that his wife had secured an annulment of their marriage.

The male nurse Gentsch, late in the evening of July 10, 1903, answered the bell of patient no. 77. He entered the cell-like room and turned to close the door. Suddenly he was hit over the head with a broom handle. The nurse was so surprised that he did not react immediately and received a second blow which knocked him unconscious. George ripped the bed sheets into strips, bound the hands and feet of the nurse and put a gag in his mouth. Then he went through his pockets, took keys and some small change, locked the room from the outside and ran quietly to a doctor's room. Here he found what he was looking for—a light summer top coat and a straw hat. He put the coat over his institution clothes, grasped a cane, and opening the handle-less doors with a pass-key, walked boldly to the main entrance and out of the building, past the saluting porter. The night was well chosen—it was raining mildly and very dark. He walked leisurely to the railway station and took a ticket to Berlin.

'I hated to hit the man,' he recollected later. 'But I had no other choice. It was a boring place and I liked neither the routine nor the food. Nor did I like the idea of spending the rest of my life in padded cells. It was too monotonous and depressing. When I read in the papers that the nurse had nothing worse than a swollen head and a slight headache, I was really glad.'

He arrived in Berlin after midnight and went straight to the boarding-house Eber in the Jaegerstrasse, to collect his clothing and an envelope Pellicio had left with 500 marks. At four in the morning he boarded a slow train for Austria. He had to change trains at Dresden and, out of sheer bravado, he walked out of the station into the hotel opposite and lifted a few suitcases in the hall waiting for early travellers. Two days later he arrived happily in Vienna and took a room in a private hotel not far from the station.

The escape from Dalldorf of arch-thief Manolesco made headlines for the whole week. The Press made the best of it, warming up all his old adventures and picturing him as the most cunning and dangerous thief ever. Soon his trail over the Austrian border was picked up, followed to Prague, Innsbruck and Vienna, and published with glee by the news-papers. The result was panic among the wealthy guests of the Bohemian Spas, of Teplitz, Marienbad, Karlsbad, of the holiday resorts in the Alps—and special precautions by the luxury hotels everywhere. In the meantime, George was sitting in Vienna and reading with pleasure about his adventures, both true and invented. He had contacted his old associate and solicitor Katz, and on his advice, went to the Vienna police to give himself up, and to ask for asylum.

As a result, a German application for extradition was rejected. George, it was maintained, was not a criminal, *he had been acquitted at his trials*. He had escaped, it was true, from an asylum, that is from a hospital. And no law existed to extradite a patient from any kind of hospital. He was set free on the condition that he reported to the police every day and did not leave the city without permission.

'It was a difficult position,' explained George later. 'I was under strict observation and therefore not able to do any kind of business. Besides the papers went on publishing stories about me, which did not help.'

Money was getting very short. His friend Katz assisted him but not enough to let him live in his old style. Then one day a letter arrived from Romania, sent by the Bucharest newspaper *Adeverul*, which asked if Monsieur George Manolesco would be prepared to write his memoirs, and offering a considerable fee. George accepted with alacrity and was invited to Bucharest, fare paid, to discuss the matter and to sign a contract. When informed that he might be arrested on entering Romania on the charge of desertion, the paper went to the trouble of straightening out that little matter with the authorities. Although George always knew that there was nothing which money could not adjust in Romania, he was still sceptical about going back. Now the Austrian authorities decided to act on an old expulsion order and to send their unwanted guest to his mother-country. He travelled to the border at State expense.

Adeverul could not miss such an opportunity as the return of George Manolesco. When he arrived in Craiova, an enormous, cheering crowd awaited him. A representative of *Adeverul* took him to an hotel, and there in the hall, an elderly, grey-haired man walked up to him with outstretched hand and a welcoming smile on his face. His Real Highness, Prince George Lahovary!

'George!' he shouted, 'if you had told me in Vienna what you were after and why, I would have given you everything you wanted with my blessing!' He slapped him on the back and shoulders like a long lost son. 'I hope you will stick to your promise and come with me to my farm.'

Unfortunately it was not possible. The newspaper representative bundled George into the morning train to the capital, where he arrived in the evening. The station square was black with people. Extra editions of *Adeverul* were on sale with a portrait of George on the front page. Cheers greeted the most famous son of Romania, the genius who had hoodwinked the world for years. Like a hero he had to appear on the balcony of his hotel room, waving to the crowds, and enjoying every second of it.

Only in one country in the world could such a welcome be given to a crook: in Romania where morals were measured differently and where a corrupt society could find unlimited delight in such a man, so long as the man was a 'gentleman', dressed in the latest fashion. Nobly-born army officers were proud of the privilege of George Manolesco's company, and he was guest of honour at their messes and clubs. He had plenty of money from his publishers, he became the darling of society and the idol of the masses, for whose rights—according to his memoirs—he fought and stole!

Quite naturally, his father, now an ex-captain and advanced to a Sous-Prefect, a subaltern post in the provincial administration, came to the capital to see his famous son. 'He was as foolish as ever,' recalled Manolesco. 'He still tried to win at cards because his conscience did not allow him to take bribes from small people to augment his income. So money was still a rare commodity in the Manolesco *ménage*, especially since Grandmother had died and there was nobody to count the pennies.' Not much love was lost between father and son, although the old Sous-Prefect embraced George and declared how much he loved him, and called him by his pet name, 'Gogu'. To get rid of him quickly, George gave him some money and sent him back to the provinces.

When his memoirs finally appeared, offers for translation rights were made by French and German publishers. George was an internationally famous personality, at the summit of fame, the darling of Bucharest, the much-sought lover of many a lady of society. His flight from Berlin had made him the man no prison could hold.

When journalists interviewed him and asked him why he had become so popular, George said: 'I do a lot of things which people would love to do, but don't because they haven't got the courage. There is a bit of larceny in everyone.'

When Kaiser Wilhelm II read this remark, along with George's memoirs, he was reported to have laughed loud and said: 'What a man! What a scoundrel! We could use a few people like that to make life more amusing in Berlin.' He was especially impressed by George's adventures as a prince, and his marriage to the Baroness. 'Serves the Saxonians right,' he said to his aide. 'What the girl needed was a good spanking, not a husband.'

Even with all the publicity, the sale of George's book was financially not the tremendous success he expected. There was a lot of criticism from medical men, judges and scientists, who branded the author as an unadulterated liar and his memoirs as whitewash for a common thief. Money became shorter and Romania consequently less affectionate. No longer did George wish to stay in Bucharest, which he called a 'big village run wild, trying to copy Paris'. Now he wanted to give up crime and concentrate all his energies on writing. Despite his expulsion he took the train to Austria for a holiday in the Tyrol. Under the name of George Mercadente he stayed for a couple of weeks in the famous old Hotel Greif in Bozen, now and then undertaking small raiding expeditions to hotels in the neighbourhood. Like all the other tourists, he wore the national costume of short leather trousers and green alpine hat with a feather, a coloured shirt and leather braces, a mountain stick, and nailed shoes.

As his money slowly vanished, newspapers he approached were not too enthusiastic about his contributions and there was little to expect from royalties which he had absorbed in generous advances. He felt it would be safer to leave Austria; the question was how, and where to go. His publishers gave him some more money because they wished to cut some chapters in his memoirs that were too scandalous even for Romania, and George decided to emigrate to the United States; there to start a new and honest life.

At the age of thirty-five, he landed in New York, this time not as a luxury passenger, but at least equipped with a genuine passport. He was an emigrant, determined to make good in the New World; in the land where almost anyone could become a millionaire; the land of unlimited possibilities; that received the flotsam of the Old World with open arms.

Chapter 13

It took George just three days to discover that the pavements of New York were most certainly not paved with gold, and that very few citizens of God's Own Country were millionaires. His entry as an emigrant was very different from the glorious arrival in the Middle West ten years before as a member of Europe's highest nobility. Luxury hotels and high society were now far out of his reach. The teeming city of gigantic buildings and millions of people ever hustling after dollars only depressed him and hampered his style. He possessed exactly seventy-two dollars and his English suits. He was lonely and badly upset that even Pellicio had deserted him and failed to reply to a letter.

The once most-notorious man in Europe was a nobody in America, and that perhaps hit him hardest. He had no friends, not even acquaintances.

In his second book of reminiscences, in which he tried to exonerate himself completely, he wrote: 'I went to America to go straight and to be honest, and I look on the years following my departure from Europe as the years of my reincarnation. I wanted to work and to make good.'

Honesty did not pay very much by George Manolesco's standards. He took a cheap room in Lower Manhattan, and went out to look for work. He began as a packer in a men's clothing warehouse on 32nd Street, but it was slavery for seven dollars a week and he left it after six days—with a smart Kuppenheimer suit worth thirty dollars. This minor theft did not conflict with George's ideas of honesty. He regarded it as a matter of simple self-preservation. His

European clothes had not met with the approval of the Americans, but only produced jeers and laughs in the boarding-house and from his workmates. Sadly he sold most of his English suits for twenty dollars, and then had his great pride, the Kaiser Wilhelm moustache, removed by an enthusiastic barber. Now outwardly normal, he got a job in an hotel on Washington Square as a dish-washer. Compared with clothes packing it was well paid, as food was free and plentiful, even if a lot less palatable than George liked. Partly because of the food but mainly because washing dishes would ruin his hands, he threw up the job after four days. But it enabled him to pass freely into the hotel, past unsuspecting detectives and porters and take a pass-key from the supervisor's office. With this he opened a room on the twelfth floor and left with $300 in his pocket.

For lack of similar opportunity, this was his only robbery from a New York hotel, but he managed to get work with the Gotham Sightseeing Corporation. Standing, megaphone in hand, in a forty-seater open tourer, he showed gullible visitors to New York the city of which he himself knew next to nothing. Even though his manners and knowledge of languages had won him the job he was fired after three days for gross incompetence, in mixing up Grant's Tomb with the Stock Exchange.

He moved to a small hotel on 45th Street off Broadway, mostly frequented by show-people and artists, many with nothing to do all day, just like George. There he made the acquaintance of a small, sturdy Hungarian with a shock of white hair, a friendly, rosy face and darting eyes. He wore top hat and frock-coat, and a gilt watch chain without a watch. The two East Europeans seized on one another, delighted to talk about all the haunts of Budapest and Vienna, Paris and Berlin, especially since they could use German or French instead of the barbaric tongue of the Yankees! He turned out to be an impresario, bound for St. Louis where the great World Fair had just opened, and for which he had imported a dozen freaks from East Europe. When the next evening George bought him a dinner of *Szeged Gulyas* and Tokay wine, he had made a friend for life.

'I like you,' said the Hungarian. 'You have an honest face. Won't you come to St. Louis and help me manage my show?' As George hesitated, he added: 'You speak the languages Romanian, Bulgarian, some Hungarian and German; you will do very well,' and promised him free board and a room in an hotel plus twenty-five dollars a week and free travel to St. Louis.

'By the way,' said the Hungarian next, 'my name is Imre Feher. What is yours?'

George told him it was George Manolesco.

Feher looked horrified for a second, pushed his top hat back in excitement, and then smiled. Without a word he took from his pocket a morning paper, opened it and spread it on the table. 'George, my friend,' he said, 'this is a very good joke,' and pointed with a fat finger to a paragraph. 'According to this, George Manolesco is being sought by the Paris police for having stolen a diamond necklace from an American visitor, yesterday morning, in Paris. Either you are a magician or you have wings to be in New York twenty-four hours later.'

This time it was George who was horrified. Then he laughed aloud. 'It was a joke,' he said. 'My name is really George Mercadente.'

'*What?!*' cried the little impresario. 'Mercadente? But *bácsi*, that is the other name of the George Manolesco man. His . . . how do you call it? . . . alias, if I may say so. He also calls himself Prince Lahovary. Haven't you read the story? What a man!'

Now George was really shocked. He later described his reaction to Feher's disclosure: 'I thought that the police would come and get me any moment. Then it dawned on me that as the story in the paper said the theft had been committed only a day previously there was no danger for me, 3,000 miles from Paris. Obviously someone had stolen some jewels somewhere, and the Paris police had automatically blamed George Manolesco, of whose whereabouts they had not the slightest clue. That was the price of fame.'

Feher looked hard now at George. 'You have a face one can trust, and I believe that with this face you might get

away with a lot. Now, tell me, are you George Manolesco . . .? What a question! Naturally you are George
Manolesco. Do not deny it. I have read so much about you
in your memoirs, that I am completely certain it is you.' He
stretched his fat hand over the table. 'Come and shake, my
friend. I am proud to meet you. I am sure we can do business
together.'

The business now suggested was to appear in St. Louis
at the side show of the Great Exhibition as the star turn in a
freak-programme—'THE GREATEST EUROPEAN
THIEF OF THE CENTURY, GEORGE MANOLESCO,
The Man no Police could Catch.'

'The hell,' thought George, and politely but firmly
declined the generous offer and settled for the post of
under-manager in 'Feher's East European Midget Show'.

Three days later Feher and George arrived in St. Louis,
together with twelve dwarfs, none higher than twenty-eight
inches. The oldest was fifty-three and a card sharper of great
skill and experience. His name was Adolar, and out of professional interest George struck up a friendship with him
from the first moment of their meeting. They competed with
each other in complicated card-tricks. There were also four
married couples; the smallest of these and the star turn in
the programme were each only twenty-six inches high;
another of the midgets, the baby of the troupe at twenty-two,
wore an Abraham Lincoln beard on his pink face. He was
studying by post to become a mechanic, and acted as Master
of Ceremonies during the show.

George's duties were very simple. He had to look after
the little folk, see to it that they did not get lost, that they
ate properly and got enough sleep, and to deal with their
complaints. Most of the midgets spoke Romanian and
German and George got on very well with them, taking
them to the fairground in the morning and back to their
lodgings in the evening. They shared ten rooms in a gigantic
wooden structure built inside the fairground and called the
'Inside Inn', which had 4,000 rooms and could sleep 6,000
guests at four dollars a head.

George and his Kindergarten, as they were soon known,

travelled every morning at eleven by Intramural railway to 'The Pike' amusement park to be ready for the first performance at noon. Then he went on to the near-by Wabash Station to collect Mr. Feher coming in from St. Louis—since he preferred a town hotel.

Feher's show tent was squeezed in between the Water Chutes and the Star-Show: 'By submarine to Paris and back by Balloon', and opposite the 'Living Picture House' and Hagenbeck's Circus.

It was an amusing and lively life, and George almost enjoyed it. If the money he earned had been better, he would have really liked it, for he had always had a weakness for show-people. Then Eugenie Parette, a slight, pretty girl employed at the Canadian Village Exhibit, spoiled things. During his fortnightly day off he took her on a boat trip up the Mississippi. She came from Quebec and was more French than the French, and very attracted to George. Between love-making, she told him of the greatness of Canada, which left George cold; but when she came to describe the Klondike gold rush and added that the State of Manitoba was giving away land to new settlers and a kind of second gold rush had started there, George listened intently. In a flash he decided to travel north at once. His decision was unexpectedly strengthened by the indiscretion of his little boss, Imre Feher.

To have discovered the famous George Manolesco in America was something the impresario could not keep to himself. It was too good to remain a secret. He told it to a reporter in St. Louis, with the result that two pressmen turned up at George's room at the Inside Inn. He was furious. He told the reporters that they were totally mistaken, that their information was utterly wrong. His real name was . . . Koenigsbrueck, and as that was rather difficult to pronounce in English he had chosen the first name that came to him. But when he was offered $250 for a story of his exploits, his need of money won. He rewrote the story of his first adventure with the Comtesse de Boulogne in Constantinople, which the Romanian publishers had carefully suppressed. It was frank and uninhibited, an impossible story for such a Puritan country as America, and the editor decided he could not print it. But George was paid and at least had his fare to the north.

There still remained Imre Feher, and of him George took his revenge for his loose talking in genuine Manolesco style. At the week-end he emptied the show cash-box, took all the takings, some $400, and boarded the morning express via Indianapolis to Detroit before the theft was discovered. Feher raised the alarm, but George was already over the Canadian border, and the St. Louis police just laughed when told that the famous George Manolesco had been in their midst. They told Imre Feher to go back home and sleep it off.

By the time he reached Montreal, George had to make some money, and seeing no opportunity to steal any, he went to a newspaper to offer them some stories. Due once more to his charm and salesmanship he was commissioned to write an article on the Paris underworld. It brought him $100, which so disappointed him that he abandoned for ever his plan of earning a living honestly by writing. It definitely did not pay. He took a train to Winnipeg *en route* for Manitoba.

Someone told him that land could be had for next to nothing up the Red River Valley and on Lake Manitoba, and he took the newly built railway north to Portage La Prairie, a French-Canadian settlement which he disliked on sight. So he went on to Gypsumville and then settled in an hotel at Alousa, a hamlet not far from Manitoba Lake and now swarming with fortune-seekers from all over the continent, including many genuine gold diggers who had found gold in Yukon and had settled around Alousa.

The first thing the clothes-conscious George did was to buy himself a fine outfit of breeches, high patent-leather riding boots and a black jacket, and then, blending into the surroundings, he established himself at the bar of the hotel as a professional gambler.

$\mathscr{C}$hapter 14

Even with but $200 in his pocket, he was once more the old confident George Manolesco, combining nerve with masculine charm, delighted to be in a village which spoke French, and which was invaded daily by characters, uncouth but friendly, easy going—and loaded with money. In his first three weeks he played baccara and poker—honestly—and made nearly $1,000 profit each week. He calculated that if he could continue to win at this rate, he could in a couple of months return to civilization, perhaps even to Europe.

Winter comes early in northern Canada, and in 1904 it was a severe one. By October roads were already nearly impassable and the streets of the small hamlet were covered with hard-frozen snow. On the very day that he received a letter from his European publishers asking for a second volume of his memoirs, he slipped on the ice while leaving the bar and broke his right arm. After an hour or so the local doctor was found half drunk in another bar, and George was carried to his wooden surgery, where his arm was set and put into plaster.

It was the beginning of the end of the Manolesco story.

George's luck had run out. The fracture, crudely set, would not mend; swelling set in and George undertook the uncomfortable and dangerous journey to Montreal to enter hospital. They did the best they could, but the damage was too serious and the only cure would have been to break the arm again and reset it. This was too much for George, who had lost all confidence in Canadian—or any other—doctors.

Out of his last $800 he bought himself a first-class ticket

on a steamer from Halifax to Cherbourg and landed back in Europe, arm in sling, at the beginning of 1905. He made his way to Paris, where he arrived with $150 and a high fever. He took a sordid little room in a hotel in the rue de l'Arcade and, feeling helpless and lost, telegraphed Pellicio for help.

Pellicio arrived within hours to find his handsome, erstwhile master in a shocking state, moaning with pain. He had had no letters from George for a long time and had given up hope of ever seeing him again.

At once he went out to buy some decent clothes for the old dandy, who now had nothing but the Wild West outfit he had worn in Canada. He did not ask any questions, he just acted. He called a barber to have George 'humanized', as he expressed it, and then took him by carriage to a doctor in the rue de la Bourse. The doctor's verdict was serious. An immediate operation offered some chance of saving the arm. But the operation was not very successful. An abscess had developed at the shoulder, and although its removal brought relief to George and he could move again without pain, his arm was now permanently crooked and had to stay in a sling.

George did not abandon hope. Bitterly he cursed his misfortune and the incompetence of doctors in general, and decided to travel to Milan where the greatest fracture-specialists in Europe practised. But there was no money and although Pellicio was only too willing to help, George would not hear of it. He dictated to Pellicio a letter to his publishers asking for an advance on a second volume of his memoirs. The publishers agreed and he even collected some money due from royalties from the first book.

He travelled hopefully to Milan and was examined by several Italian specialists, but nothing could be done at the moment, and on their advice he went to Pallanza on Lake Maggiore for a complete rest.

Although he was now a gaunt caricature of his former handsome appearance, he was beautifully dressed after a shopping spree in Milan and his allure for women remained undiminished. In addition, in this holiday spa George Manolesco was *still* famous and intriguing. His memoirs had been read by most people, and now his illness and sad incapacity made him ever more interesting to the sort of women he had pursued all his life.

It was in Pallanza that he made the acquaintance of Mademoiselle Pauline Tollet, holidaying with her mother. She was twenty-four, a well-built, lively brunette, likeable and energetic, and she fell very hard for the poor sick young man. Her father, a French engineer, had died leaving her a substantial fortune. George, depressed by his illness, was for once quite uninterested in any kind of romantic adventure, but Pauline was determined to attract his attention and perhaps love. She attached herself inexorably to George, mothering him, writing his letters, cutting his food. Never before had George experienced unselfish care. Pauline was both tender and firm, and George developed not love but affection and gratitude for the vivacious French girl, and did nothing to fight her growing influence over him. When she asked if he really was the famous George Manolesco, he told her without hesitation. Soon she knew nearly all his adventures and was proud of the confidence of such a great man. It was Pauline who actually proposed marriage.

During the autumn of 1905 George Manolesco and Pauline Tollet became engaged. George was happy, not only because Pauline was the most devoted, helpful, adoring female he had ever encountered, but also because she had told him that her father had left her enough money to live without worry for a long time to come. 'And then,' she added, 'you will be better and we can certainly make some money honestly without stealing.' His future mother-in-law had no objection to the curious alliance of her daughter with a notorious thief, and the wedding was fixed for January 1906.

Then in December 1905, George's arm gave more trouble; two big abscesses developed and it was decided to take him to hospital in Milan. There the specialists decided on an immediate operation, which took place in the *Casa di Salute*. Pauline could hardly be moved from his bedside. Although the doctors insisted that the arm could not be saved, she proclaimed that she would marry him, two arms or one. She kept her word.

In March 1906 George's arm was amputated in Paris and in the summer Pauline and George were married, with Pellicio as one of the witnesses. She wrote to George's publishers: 'Vous comprenez alors mon immense chagrin de l'état actual de mon fiancé; mais advienne que pourra, mon affection envers lui ne changerai jamais.'*

Now George and Pauline settled down in Milan. He was nearing his thirty-sixth birthday, and he knew that never again would he be able to steal or cheat at cards, even if he wished to. Genuinely now he had no desire for crime; the experiences and sufferings of the past year had utterly changed him. He was at last in love with his self-sacrificing wife. He had no financial worries, for they lived comfortably, if not in Grand Hotel style. Still he wanted to do something unusual, to be famous.

He chose an ironic, but not untypical way. He persuaded a Milan newspaper to let him write a series of articles on, of all things, how to keep property safe in hotels—from men like George Manolesco. Useless to him now, he betrayed all the tricks of his trade, clinically analysing the psychology of robbing the rich, and making life very difficult indeed for his imitators and successors—which in itself gave him considerable pleasure. The fact that he was helping his old enemies, the police of half a dozen countries, did rankle a little, but . . . money was money, and his name in the paper once more was better still.

He wrote his new book *Shipwrecked* solemnly, seriously, quite convinced he was giving the world an important work; and when he had collected enough Italian Press reviews, he sent them to his German publisher, unabashed by, for instance, Corriere della Sera's comment: 'He is a rebel against society, without shame or remorse, quite unwilling to forget his former crimes.'

He was delighted to hear that a racehorse had been named after him; he wanted to act in a stage play of his own adventures (nothing came of that), and his vanity was flattered as never before when it was suggested to him,

* 'You will understand my worry about the state of my fiancé; but come what may, my affections for him will never change.'

perhaps somewhat maliciously, that his brain, so brilliant and so interesting, should be investigated after his death by the new school of Italian criminologists working under Professor Lombroso. At once he dictated to the rather appalled Pauline a letter to his publishers asking them to buy future rights in his head for the immediate payment of 6,000 francs!

The strange marriage went surprisingly well. George said in a Press interview: 'My wife believes in me, and who am I to deceive her? She loves me because I withstood danger, and I love her because of her tenderness and pity.'

Perhaps Pauline really believed George to be a genius, as he had been called by several journalists. Whatever it was, they were devoted to one another. But their money did not last long enough. George always elegant again now, and considered one of the best-dressed men in Milan, had but a tiny income from journalism and they soon had to economize and move into more modest quarters. For quite a time George continued to receive wide publicity, if not much money. Again and again the Italian police decided that he had committed some particularly audacious robbery and investigated roughly and thoroughly, to George's fury. When in 1907 he became ill and had to take to his bed, he read about the theft of the State Regalia from Dublin Castle, smiled contentedly and said: 'That is one theft they cannot charge me with.'

Pauline had a son on February 8, 1907, and he was christened Claude. Again George was deliriously happy, and developed a strong desire to see his almost forgotten daughter again. That wish was never fulfilled. An insidious illness confined him to bed until the day of his death in 1911, by which time George was a forgotten man.

Shortly before his death news reached him that his first wife, Angelika, and his daughter Jeanne Manolesco, had been granted permission to drop George's name for ever. Instead the King of Saxonia gave them a new and honourable name granting them titles of nobility as von Otterschuetz.

During George Manolesco's twenty years as 'Prince of Thieves' he stole in all about £3,000,000 in present values. When he died, all he owned was fifty Italian lire outstanding, for a contribution to an Italian newspaper. To the last day of his life he never omitted to shave and have his hair dressed by his devoted wife.

After his death twelve suits, forty silk shirts, ten pairs of patent-leather shoes and all the other accessories of the prosperously equipped gentleman were enshrined in a room by his widow, together with notes for further memoirs . . . and his silver-framed patent of Valebianco's nobility.

J. J. LYNX

J. J. Lynx, born in Berlin at the turn of the century, is the author of nine books (which have been published in France, England, Germany, Holland and Sweden). He first became interested in Manolesco when he wrote a serial on criminals for a Continental paper while he was working as a correspondent in Vienna. Among his friends at that time was a detective working for the Vienna C.I.D. and, with his help, Lynx proceeded with the documentation of Manolesco —which had now become one of his major hobbies—and from official and unofficial sources a picture of *The Prince of Thieves* was gradually built up.